Science: Level 3

U316 The environmental web

Book 1 Environmental Changes: Global Challenges

Edited by Mark Brandon and Nigel Clark with contributions from Mike Widdowson

This publication forms part of the Open University course U316 *The environmental web*. The complete list of texts which make up this course can be found on the back cover. Details of this and other Open University courses can be obtained from the Student Registration and Enquiry Service, The Open University, PO Box 197, Milton Keynes MK7 6BJ, United Kingdom (tel. +44 (0)845 300 60 90; email general-enquiries@open.ac.uk).

Alternatively, you may visit the Open University website at www.open.ac.uk where you can learn more about the wide range of courses and packs offered at all levels by The Open University.

To purchase a selection of Open University course materials visit www.ouw.co.uk, or contact Open University Worldwide, Walton Hall, Milton Keynes MK7 6AA, United Kingdom for a brochure (tel. +44 (0)1908 858793; fax +44 (0)1908 858787; email ouw-customer-services@open.ac.uk).

The Open University
Walton Hall, Milton Keynes
MK7 6AA

First published 2003. Second edition 2009.

Edited and designed by The Open University.

Typeset by SR Nova Pvt. Ltd, Bangalore, India.

Printed in the United Kingdom by Halstan Printing Group, Amersham.

The paper used in this publication is procured from forests independently certified to the level of Forest Stewardship Council (FSC) principles and criteria. Chain of custody certification allows the tracing of this paper back to specific forest-management units (see www.fsc.org).

ISBN 978 1 8487 3007 6

2.1

Contents

Chapter 1
Shrinking worlds: islands and environmental change

1.1   Introducing *The environmental web*

People and places around the world are being drawn into closer contact. We are getting used to the idea that money, goods, people and ideas flow around the planet with a speed and intensity that would have been surprising even 50 years ago. Many people are also becoming aware that there is a price to pay for this relentless activity; a cost that must be borne by the life-support systems of the Earth. Initially appearing as an unfortunate side effect of our way of life, environmental problems now loom large in the way we perceive and experience the world. No sooner had we begun to conceive of our planet as a 'whole' – a single, interconnected system – than it became apparent that this system was under duress – stirred, shaken and disturbed by our human interventions. Today, environmental problems and 'global' consciousness have become inseparable.

Sooner or later, most environmental problems flow over the boundaries of our neighbourhoods, our counties and even our countries. Some are fully global in both cause and effect. The possibility that human activities are collectively transforming the climate of the entire planet must surely be one of the most perturbing messages that humankind has ever had to confront. Quite suddenly, it seems, we are having to grapple with the knowledge that emissions from the energy we consume in our work and play directly impact on people and other living things on the far side of the planet – and will continue to do so long after we are gone. In a less direct way, through the workings of the global economy, many of our actions have repercussions elsewhere in the world. The materials we work with, the products we buy and the investments we make affect people and their environments half a world away.

Viewed in this way, the scale and complexity of environmental issues can seem overwhelming, as if to thwart and belittle any intention we have to take positive action. But the pathways and connections that weave everyone into the wider world can do more than simply submit us to forces beyond our control. Many of the ties that bind us into the global economy can also bring us into contact with other people, who share our feelings and concerns, and they can give us access to information and tools that can help us turn our intentions into actions. Over the same decades in which the world seems to have shrunk and its environmental problems grown, people have begun to cooperate in new ways – locally, nationally and around the planet. Some of these new modes of meeting and making decisions involve government officials and scientific experts. But other new forms of communication and cooperative action involve groups of ordinary individuals; people whose experiences, insights and ideas seem to form a more 'everyday' world. Today, there is a growing feeling that ordinary people working together can, and should, make a difference to the way global problems are dealt with and to the way the world is run.

The environmental web is about understanding and looking after the life forms and landforms we depend on. It is about understanding, and responding to, the environmental challenges we face, from our backyards to the entire globe. And it is about making sense of connections that bind the local and the global, so that we might make these linkages work for us and for the sort of world we want to live in. As you may have guessed, the title *The environmental web* conjures up different sorts of interconnectivity. It refers to ecological 'webs' – the weave of living organisms, cycles of matter and flows of energy that make up the natural world. It also refers to the networks and exchanges that our species has added to the world: the patterns of connectivity that make up our social realm.

It has never been easy to define what is meant by 'nature' or 'the natural world' and 'society' or 'the social world', and it is getting harder all the time. This course takes 'society' or 'the social world' to mean all those processes and products that human agency has brought into the world, and 'nature' or 'the natural world' to mean those forms and processes that came into existence before, or independently of, human agency. In this sense, all human social achievements ultimately rely on natural processes or resources. At the same time, the more that social agency transforms the world, the more difficult it becomes to identify or describe a 'nature' that is distinct from 'society'.

The environmental web deals with the entanglement of the natural and the social by treating nature and society as different, but interrelated, systems. A **system** means any group of parts or components that interact with each other, in such a way that any change made to one part will affect at least some of the other parts. Some systems – such as a family of human beings or the Solar System – have a few 'components'; but most of the systems considered in this course – such as ecosystems, climate systems and social systems – have many parts (Figure 1.1a, b).

Figure 1.1   Two examples of systems with many parts: (a) an aerial view of a 'spaghetti junction' road network; (b) a braided river in Siberia.

■   Think of three other systems you have dealings with in your everyday life.

☐   There are many possibilities: for example an institution such as a workplace or a school. These come under the category of social systems. You might have thought of technological systems, such as gadgets or machines, or a physical system, such as your body.

Thinking about systems makes it easier to come and go from the natural world to the social world, and to move between different scales – from the microscopic to the global – without losing our bearings. Rather than thinking about nature and society as separate spheres, they are conceived of as interlinked systems, at least partially open to each other and in constant exchange.

Thinking in terms of 'systems' focuses attention on the connections between parts or individuals or groups, and helps us to recognise that relationships are as important as the parts themselves. Over recent decades, new information and communications technologies (ICTs) have helped to bring this lesson home – by giving increasing numbers of people the chance to experience a form of interconnectivity that is unprecedented in its capacity to bring distant people and places into conversation. The course title – *The environmental web* – alludes to these new modes of electronic connectivity, their impact on the world, and their potential for engaging with environmental issues in novel ways.

While other means of communicating, such as print, television broadcasting and face-to-face encounters, lose none of their importance, new technologies have a capacity to combine the advantages of other media. By linking computers, telephones and databases into a global network, the internet allows us to search and retrieve stored information, and to share our knowledge, thoughts and experiences with like-minded people wherever they are in the world. ICTs can help us respond to environmental problems on the same terrain they present themselves. That is, if the problems we are facing link the local with the global in dense and complicated ways, we must make the most of tools that enable our learning and action to likewise form far-reaching interconnections, bridging the local and the global.

'The Internet', as one activist put it, 'has become the latest, greatest arrow in our quiver of social activism' (cited in French, 2000, p. 163). What greatly appeals to many internet users is that no single group or organisation controls the content or the development of the new networks. For many people, this adds to the feeling that their own participation in ICT-mediated exchanges is part of a turn towards popular or 'grassroots' involvement in important events.

1.2   Connected planet, divided world

The term frequently used to capture all the processes that are bringing different parts of the globe into closer connection, and to convey the experience of the planet as a single place, is **globalisation**. Environmental problems are part of the process of globalisation but, at the same time, other forms of global interconnectivity play an important role in the way people experience and respond to environmental issues. Globalisation is the first of the four key themes or concepts running through this course. The others, which are introduced in the next two chapters, are sustainability, uncertainty and governance. These terms are used frequently in the arena of environmental thought and action: each offers a handle on an important aspect of environmental problems and problem solving. But at the same time, they also direct our attention to major fault lines in environmental thought and practice – to the points that are most debated and contested.

One of the tensions running through the concept of globalisation is that it conjures a sense of unity and oneness but, at the same time, it encompasses deep divisions. In thinking of the planet as an interconnected whole, there is a temptation to think of everyone as 'being in the same boat'. But, as much as they draw us together, environmental problems and other forms of global interconnectedness are played out in a very uneven world. Some people are more vulnerable to environmental threats and disasters than others. And those most at risk often have the least access to the resources and tools that could make their lives safer and easier. Just as we tend to speak of the 'whole Earth' and the 'endangered Earth' in the same breath, so too have global environmental issues and worldwide inequity become deeply entangled. Several terms are commonly used as shorthand for these divides: the 'First' and the 'Third Worlds', 'the North' and 'the South', the 'developed' and the 'underdeveloped' world, the 'West' and the rest. None of these terms captures the complications and nuances of global inequality, yet each conveys something of the vast imbalances in wealth, power and opportunity that rend social life at many levels around the planet (Figures 1.2 and 1.3).

Figure 1.2 How the Independent Commission on International Development Issues divided the world in 1980. This division between a rich 'North' and a poor 'South' is now seen as oversimplistic and outdated.

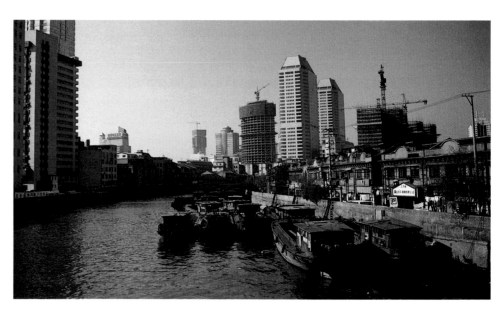

Figure 1.3 Suzhou Creek, Shanghai, China: a place where the 'developed' and the 'underdeveloped' worlds overlap.

The collision between issues of environmental degradation and questions of global inequality is one of the greatest challenges faced by the contemporary world. Put simply, the problem is this: the message from environmentalists is that current levels of global industrial activity are having serious long-term impacts on the planet. However, the benefits of industrial development have been unevenly distributed, favouring the wealthier 'developed' countries. Many of the people who speak for the less-developed world make strong claims that the benefits from the exploitation of the planet's resources should not be restricted to a minority of the world's population. Unfortunately, should all, or even most, of the rest of the world attain the level of material consumption of the wealthy minority (which itself shows no sign of levelling off), the strains on the already stressed planet will be vastly increased. Although not always in the foreground, this dilemma is a central part of the framework of this course.

Ideally, new forms of communication should help people all around the world share knowledge and experiences about the predicaments they are in. Moreover, the rapid dissemination of news of dangers and disasters could help the most vulnerable people. But the same connections that might help us respond to the plight of others can also make the world a more turbulent and uncontrollable place. Whatever form our ideals about a more balanced world might take, there is little doubt that new forms of electronic interconnectivity make it harder to regulate the flow of information, images, money and goods around the planet. In a world that is subject to such rapid change, every new opportunity brings costs and risks. Today, we might also speak of a 'digital divide' to highlight the unequal access to ICT around the world.

The environmental web takes a global view of environmental issues and the tools and strategies available to address these issues. However, the whole planet in all its complexity is more than anyone can handle. This course ventures into the global terrain in stages, beginning in this book with two examples: small oceanic islands and the continent of Antarctica. These may seem like exotic locations, and you may wonder why they have been chosen. It is hoped that you will recognise quite early on that where you live and apparently exotic locations elsewhere are linked in some quite extraordinary ways, and that nowhere is too distant or different to have profound relevance for your own location – and, of course, vice versa. Environmental thought and action involves a kind of journeying, and these journeys require some quite imaginative leaps in space and, moreover, in time, as you will see later.

Oceanic islands are an excellent starting point because of their extreme vulnerability to certain sorts of global environmental change. But these islands are not simply vulnerable places. Their human and non-human inhabitants are far more than victims-in-waiting. Through studying islands, we can also learn about the creative forces in both the natural and social realms. Although small oceanic islands may at first seem a world away, they can teach us about what happens on larger islands such as the British Isles or even on continents.

Antarctica might seem like an odd introduction to environmental issues, given that it has no indigenous human population. What could we learn about the relationship between humans and nature in a place that seems to have so much of the latter and so few of the former? But the fact that Antarctica – along with the freezing Southern Ocean that surrounds it – falls outside the jurisdiction of any one nation makes it a very interesting case study for the way that humankind deals with the places we have in common. At one time, the seas, islands and coastlines of Antarctica were the site of some of the most extreme overexploitation by humans of natural resources ever witnessed. But on a more positive note, as you will see, Antarctica (Figure 1.4) and the Southern Ocean show the way humankind can collectively protect its shared or common spaces.

Figure 1.4   A view of the Antarctic Peninsula.

Working through the island example you will encounter several interrelated environmental problems. You will return to each of these problems and the questions they raise in greater depth later in the course. Along the way, you will meet (or be reminded about) some of the skills and techniques for tracking down information that you will need for the course. By the end of this book, you should have a feel for the severity and complexity of environmental problems, and you will have had a taste of the interdisciplinary approach that defines this course.

1.3   Troubled waters: the predicament of islands

Figure 1.5   The idyllic vision of a tropical island.

How does the idea of suddenly being transported to a tropical island sound? If all your responsibilities were taken care of, how would you feel about being whisked away right now – if only for a while? What ideas and images go through your mind when you think about tropical islands? If you live under the grey skies of Northern Europe, sunshine and sandy beaches probably come to mind (Figure 1.5). But is there more to it than this? If travel literature and tourist brochures are anything to go by, much of the attraction of tropical islands is about 'getting away from it all' – putting your feet up, and putting some distance between yourself and your busy, everyday life.

There seems to be something about crossing an ocean, about landing somewhere separated by a good stretch of sea from where you live and your normal life, that has a deep appeal. This appeal seems to apply no less to people in the British Isles, which of course are large islands. The further from home you go, the more chance there is that your island experience, or your island imagining, is coloured by ideas of going somewhere 'unspoilt', a place somehow made remote by water and by distance from the woes and cares of civilisation.

> Imagine an undisturbed lush green tropical forest. Exotic tropical blooms and ripe luscious fruits. The music of birds calling out to each other. The gentle sound of wind rustling the leaves. The rushing of waves to shore in the background – the perfect tropical symphony. To many it may seem a form of paradise.
>
> (Palm Beach, Maldives, 1997)

This is how the Maldives, a cluster of islands in the Indian Ocean, try to advertise in literature and websites in order to convey the idea of an island paradise.

It is hard to deny the appeal, especially when it is raining and life's responsibilities are pressing. But it is tricky to achieve 'paradise', even if you have a tropical island at your disposal. If you have ever visited a beach resort that plays on its beautiful scenery and 'getting away from it all', or if you have heard tales from people who have, you may have a feeling for the fine line such attractions tread. A tourist resort is there to make money and, generally, the more tourists and the more facilities to accommodate tourists there are, the more money is made. Hence the 'holiday in hell' stories – when the 'idyllic' beachfront hotel turns out to be next to a building site, clattering with activity from dawn until dusk (Figure 1.6). Every developer knows the risk: not enough development and money-making opportunities are lost; too much development and the charm that attracted visitors could be lost for ever.

As someone with an interest in the environment, you are probably aware that this 'development' is about more than selling charm or preserving scenery. It is about balancing facilities with demands on resources. More visitors and more infrastructure means mounting pressure on the environment and all the services it provides. This is the tension between development and preserving the environment and, on a small island with limited space, this tension can be extreme.

Now you can learn more about these dilemmas by visiting the Maldives, the islands which include the Palm Beach resort that was selling its charms above. The following readings and activity are an essential part of this chapter, and will give you a grounding for thinking about the link between development and the environment.

Figure 1.6 Tourist development – or over development?

Read the newspaper articles about the Maldives, 'A thousand isles from nowhere', followed by 'Climate change will endanger low-lying island states' which are on the course website. Newspapers date quickly but the issues raised in these articles are likely to be relevant for the foreseeable future. As you read, think about the tension between tourist development and preserving the environment that both writers refer to, and take note of the way these issues are being addressed in the Maldives.

Activity 1.1 The view from the Maldives

Now consider your first reactions to these articles. Recall your response to the earlier idea of imagining a quick getaway to a balmy, unspoilt tropical island. Have these accounts of the Maldives changed the way you think about tropical islands? Or were you already familiar with global climate change?

The issues raised in these articles are considered in more depth later but, for now, just write down your initial feelings.

For example:

- How would you feel about living with the uncertainty about the future that the Maldivian people face?
- Do you feel a connection between where you live and the way you live, and the predicament of the Maldivian people?

Comment

You might have felt sympathy for the Maldivian people. Perhaps you also felt concern for your own situation, a creeping sense that the risks and uncertainties experienced by people on small oceanic islands might one day be facing you. Did you wonder about the impact of your lifestyle and how this contributes – negatively or positively – to the lives of people elsewhere? You might have recalled that the fantasy of 'getting away from it all' has much to do with escaping your normal, everyday responsibilities. Perhaps the plight of small island people suggested another sort of 'responsibility': whether people in one part of the world can be held responsible for the plight of others in distant places.

Another reaction to these articles could be a desire to be better informed. Strong claims are being made, but also some considerable uncertainties about the future of low-lying islands like the Maldives. You might well have wished for more evidence about what is happening to the environment and about what is likely to happen in the future. These ideas are considered further later in this chapter.

1.3.1 When sustainability met development

Setting aside the question of global climate change for the moment, focus on the way the Maldivian people are dealing with the development of their tourist industry and its environmental implications. The two newspaper articles you read were written by journalists from different countries – one British and the other from the Maldives – and they seem to have dissimilar intentions and different audiences in mind. Nevertheless, they agree that the Maldivian people are taking the relationship between tourist development and environmental protection very seriously (Figure 1.7).

Figure 1.7 A tourist resort in the Maldives designed and built following environmental guidelines.

■ Recall five ways in which the Maldivian people are attempting to minimise the environmental impacts of tourism.

☐ 1   They limit tourist development to certain islands.

2   On these islands development is restricted to 20% of the total surface area.

3   There are limits on the height of buildings (the height of a mature palm tree).

4   There are restrictions on removing vegetation and on damage to the marine environment.

5   There are strict standards for managing water and waste.

Clearly, the Maldivian people are counting on their tourist industry for revenue, and therefore to assist **development**. The term 'development' means the attainment of chosen social and economic goals by a social group (in this context, a country). The Maldivian people are taking measures to ensure that the growth of the tourist industry does not undermine the environmental resources or idyllic scenery that are their attraction. Reading between the lines, it also seems that this careful management of the tourist industry is also intended to protect the culture of the islands – especially the Islamic way of life – from foreign influences.

■ What term did President Gayoom use to describe the tourist development strategy in the Maldives?

☐ Sustainability.

Sustainability is the second of the four key course themes. 'Sustainability' means the capacity to live without undermining the systems that support life. Not surprisingly, this has emerged as one of the central issues of contemporary environmentalism. One way of framing the sustainability issue is to ask whether we can leave our children, grandchildren or generations further down the line with an environment of the same quality, or better, than our own.

The link between sustainability and development sounds straightforward. Development that does not undermine its own foundations is more desirable than development that destroys the environmental or cultural resources it relies on. Today, sustainable development dominates discussions of the global environmental predicament, but it is more complex and contested than it first appears. Where sustainability alludes primarily to concerns about long-term environmental degradation, development refers to the issue of the differences in wealth and power that divide the world's nations – and the need to address this gap. Linking these two themes together requires an explicit connection between the environmental issues and global economic inequality. This connection has not always been obvious or apparent, and you should be mindful that not everyone is happy with the way the link has been forged.

When environmental concerns were raised in the 1960s, most attention was fixed on conditions in the wealthiest and most developed countries, or on single environmental issues such as pollution or saving the great whales. It was in these countries that the negative impacts of industry and industrialised agriculture and fishing seemed most apparent. Many of the pioneer environmentalists of the 1960s and 1970s argued that the ever-increasing economic growth that everyone seemed to take for granted must eventually come up against the limits of a finite planet. The conclusion usually drawn from this observation was that the notion of 'progress' based on limitless growth – an idea at the heart of modern western civilisation – was due for a complete overhaul.

This was not a popular message for most governments or for the international business community – who clearly saw their interests lying in further economic growth. The idea of absolute limits to growth was particularly unappealing to leaders of 'the South' or the 'less-developed world' who saw it as a threat to their aspirations to bring their own economies to the level of the wealthier countries. This issue came up at the United Nations Conference on the Human Environment held in Stockholm in 1972: environmentalism's full debut on the international political stage. Less-developed countries were reassured by the rest of the world community that the 'no-growth' option would not be seriously considered. Stockholm gave rise to the first formal declaration that development and environmental concern were expected to go hand-in-hand. It was, however, a rather brief and vague pronouncement.

It was over a decade later that the union between sustainability and development was fully cemented. The World Commission on Environment and Development (WCED), set up by the United Nations in 1983, brought the notion of **sustainable development** into prominence. Sustainable development emerged as a catchphrase for a qualitatively new sort of economic growth that would minimise human impacts on the environment and greatly improve the living standards of the majority of the world's people. WCED's official report *Our Common Future* gave a definition that remains influential:

> Sustainable development seeks to meet the needs and aspirations of the present without compromising the ability to meet those of the future. Far from requiring the cessation of economic growth, it recognizes that the problems of poverty and underdevelopment cannot be solved unless we have a new era of growth in which developing countries play a large role and reap large benefits … policymakers guided by the concept of sustainable development will necessarily work to assure that growing economies remain firmly attached to their ecological roots and that these roots are protected. Environmental protection is thus inherent in the concept of sustainable development …

> (WCED, 1987, p. 40)

The idea of sustainable development now has a hold on the imagination of many environmentally aware people worldwide. The sensible and proactive way in which the Maldivian people manage their tourist industry is one of many attempts to put the idea into practice. But arguably, the dilemma that brought sustainability and development together has never disappeared. The concept has been further explored, pulled apart, redefined and even accused of being a contradiction in terms! To see what is at stake, the next section returns to the two articles on the Maldives.

1.3.2   Sustainability and global environmental change

You will need no reminding that the environmental issue that most worries the Maldivian people is changes in the Earth's climate. Both the articles you read earlier refer to arguments that human activities are contributing to an overall warming of the planet. Human interventions may well have had impacts on climate in the past, but never before has there been such widespread and popular awareness about this phenomenon. Clearly, your perceptions of the current situation depend on where in the world you are living – and global climate change may not initially strike you as a 'problem' at all. It is worth pausing and trying to remember the first time you heard about 'global warming'. Was it frightening? Or was there perhaps some appeal in the idea?

One consequence of global warming, for instance, is that the British Isles could have a more Mediterranean climate with rain falling in milder, shorter winters, and longer drier summers. By contrast, areas of North Africa will experience increased heat and aridity leading to desertification, whilst Bangladesh may be affected by increased frequency of flooding.

Similarly, living on a low-lying island gives a rather different perspective on climate change.

■ From the newspaper articles, what four problems related to climate change are facing the Maldives?

☐ 1   An increase in extreme weather events – including storm surges.

   2   Coastal erosion, possibly even the total inundation of islands.

   3   Saltwater contamination of ground freshwater supplies (aquifers).

   4   Damage to coral reefs and general, widespread disturbance of marine ecosystems.

For all their efforts at the local level, the Maldivian people are extremely vulnerable to global environmental changes which they can do little about (Figure 1.8). These changes could not only undo their own efforts at sustainable development but also completely destroy their own environment. Book 3 returns to the issue of climate change in more depth but, for now, it is enough to say that overall energy use around the planet determines the human contribution to climate change. In this regard, the Maldives' contribution to global energy use is tiny and, therefore, out of all proportion to the costs they appear to be facing.

Figure 1.8   Scene on a tropical island during a cyclone.

The dilemma of the Maldives highlights the tension that gave rise to the concept of sustainable development in the first place. At the same time, however, it points to the tensions that remain unresolved. When the WCED was attempting to reconcile development and sustainability, global climate change was already on the agenda. The WCED was aware that consuming fossil fuels, as well as cutting and burning forests, was resulting in a build-up of carbon dioxide in the Earth's atmosphere, which would trap solar radiation and result in global warming. *Our Common Future* raised the prospect of climatic change upsetting global agricultural production, together with sea-level rises devastating low-lying areas – and all within the next half-century. Clearly, the patterns of energy use that had played such an important part in the economic growth of the most developed countries could not be replicated in the less-developed countries without dire environmental consequences.

However, as you saw above, representatives of the less-developed world presented the case that the benefits accruing from the exploitation of global resources should be for everyone. This was taken to mean that less-developed countries had a right to pursue the pattern of economic development that had worked for the developed economies. At the same time, it was becoming apparent that many of the places likely to suffer the most from climate change, such as river deltas and low-lying islands and atolls, were in the less-developed world. As in the case of the Maldives, this meant that people who had not yet made a large contribution to global energy use, or shared most of its benefits, were likely to suffer most from the negative impacts of economic growth.

The WCED calculated the increase in industrial output that would be necessary to raise the production and consumption levels of the less-developed world to those of the developed world. Assuming – or rather, hoping – that the world population would stop growing in the 21st century, it concluded that a *five- to tenfold* increase in the existing global industrial outputs would be required (WCED, 1987, p. 15). And remember, this was the prognosis of environmentally aware advisers and experts, not sceptics of environmental change. Taking into account that levels of production in the 1980s were below those of today, it is worth stopping and thinking about the environmental implications of multiplying overall global energy use and raw material consumption (along with all the associated emissions and waste products) by even the lower estimate of fivefold.

Don't worry about calculations, just consider whether the world that might result would provide future generations with the same or better environmental conditions than are experienced today. Keep this in mind when you encounter the idea of sustainable development.

Despite its clear preference for an alternative to the 'limits-to-growth' idea, the WCED could not entirely evade the message of earlier environmentalists that the Earth was essentially finite. As its report conceded:

> The ultimate limits to global development are perhaps determined by the availability of energy resources and the biosphere's capacity to absorb the by-products of energy use.

(WCED, 1987, p. 58)

As sketched out in *Our Common Future*, sustainable development was an attempt to imagine a way out of this bind. Economic growth would proceed, but it would be uncoupled from the excessive use of non-renewable energy and materials. The proposals hinged mostly on increasing the efficiency of production, in particular replacing non-renewable fuels with renewable energy sources that do not contribute to global warming. This is discussed in depth in Book 3. At this stage it is important that you get a sense of the immensity of the dilemma that 'fuelled' the idea of sustainable development. This understanding is vital when considering where we stand in this quandary today.

1.3.3   The ongoing challenge of sustainability

The Maldives may be exceptional in their vulnerability to environmental change, but what does their predicament tell us about the tension between development and sustainability? It is still early in the course to be pondering problems of this complexity, but the situation prompts several ideas and questions.

Now is a good time to go to the course website and do the activities associated with Chapter 1.

Perhaps the most obvious response is that the tensions between sustainability and development are as acute today as when the WCED wrote its report in the 1980s. The climate change issue has grown, and yet there still seems to be faith in the idea that development can, and should, continue. Tension appears to be strongest between the local level – over which the Maldivian people have some degree of influence or control – and the global level – where they have little or no control. The problem, as you might have noted, is that these global changes have profound local effects.

What sort of questions does this conflict raise? There appear to be many unknowns about issues that threaten the Maldives and other low-lying areas. Will the sea level rise? If so, by how much and how fast? Are the observed changes caused by human impacts or other causes? If dramatic changes are going to occur over the next century, what are the implications for the Maldives and other vulnerable low-lying coastal areas? If people who have benefited from intensive energy use are in some sense responsible for global environmental changes, what demands might the Maldivian people make of them? And what kinds of response could be made?

It is useful to see how a simple-sounding dilemma quickly gives rise to a cascade of questions. These types of question will be posed throughout the course, and you will be offered the kind of resources and skills you need to set about addressing them. The aim is also to stimulate your curiosity and encourage you to formulate your own questions! Note that there has been no talk of 'solving' environmental problems. This does not mean they are insoluble but the issues *are* complex and tangled. All human actions are likely to have unforeseen as well as anticipated consequences. Solutions have a way of generating new problems, just as some problems can have surprising benefits, when viewed from a different perspective.

The next section looks more closely at the environmental changes that haunt both the articles on the Maldives. It starts by asking what we need to know in order to assess the claims being made about global warming and sea-level change. What sort of information do we need in order to make decisions and take effective action? Who has the knowledge or the information we require? Are all the data we need available? And what happens when information sources or knowledge claims turn out to be conflicting?

1.4   Global environmental change: substantiating the charges

Our fear of world-threatening cataclysms such as great floods have a long and colourful history. What sets contemporary environmental concerns apart is an insistence on evidence to back up claims and predictions. When we think of ourselves as 'modern', a large part of this self-definition rests on the fact that we now use science rather than other kinds of stories – such as myths or religion – to explain the way our world works. The modern trust in science hinges on the procedures through which knowledge claims are made and evaluated, rather than on the personal authority of whoever voiced the claims. When the President of the Maldives made a statement to the global community, it is not surprising that he sought to support his claim with reference to scientific evidence. In the newspaper article he announced, 'The IPCC has established that human activities are changing the world's climate system'. But who, or what, is the IPCC? What are its aims and recommendations, and on what grounds can it claim knowledge about the trends in climate of the entire Earth?

It may seem obvious that scientific evidence is needed to assess a claim about an environmental problem, or at least to give this assessment legitimacy. However, it has not always been this straightforward. In the 1960s and 1970s many environmentalists viewed the achievements of science as being heavily implicated in the 'environmental crisis' – and there were appeals for the rejection of the so-called 'scientific world view'. There is, perhaps, something to be said for this critique of applied science, and some 'greens' and environmentalists still remain deeply sceptical about the uses to which scientific knowledge has been put. Yet, at the same time, we should be mindful that the modern environmental movement itself is highly dependent on scientific evidence in order to substantiate its claims. Moreover, in many, if not the majority of, cases it has been concerned *scientists* who have played the pivotal role in bringing environmental issues to public attention. In the 1980s, as concern over the environment crystallised into the concept of 'global environmental change', voices calling for the wholehearted rejection of scientific values faded into the margins of environmental thought and practice.

You will discover and learn about the IPCC soon but, first, here is an easy question. If you wanted to test claims about global warming, how would you go about taking the temperature of the planet? In fact, this is not an easy question at all. Climate varies both spatially (from region to region) and temporally (most obviously by time of day and season), so there is no single or simple way to measure global temperature. It is necessary to compile many measurements of air temperature (Figure 1.9) made over time and in different places and derive an 'average'.

Figure 1.9   A Stevenson screen: a specialised box (height and width is 50 cm) containing meteorological instruments, including those for measuring air temperature.

A regional example of this process of compilation was the Asia–Pacific Network for Global Change Research Workshop held in New Zealand in 2001. Meteorologists from around the Pacific brought their national measurements together to produce a composite picture of Pacific climate from 1950 to 2000. According to the convenor, climate scientist Jim Salinger, the results showed a higher than expected warming in the South Pacific, and, that whilst the global average temperature rose by 0.6 °C during the past century, temperatures in the Pacific rose more than this in the past 50 years alone. The daily temperature records of Australia, the Cook Islands, Fiji, French Polynesia, New Caledonia, the Solomon Islands and Vanuatu show a rise of 0.5–1.0 °C in the second half of the 20th century; elsewhere in the Pacific, the warming was closer to that of the global average. As Salinger, rather sardonically, concluded on behalf of his fellow workshop participants, 'global warming is alive and well'.

But is it? The Pacific covers a vast area, but how can we tell if warming in this region is typical of the whole planet? This is where the Intergovernmental Panel on Climate Change (IPCC) comes in. Amid growing scientific concern about the Earth's climate during the 1970s and 1980s, the Panel was established in 1988 by the World Meteorological Organization (WMO) and the United Nations Environment Programme (UNEP), which are two organisations of the United Nations (UN). The IPCC now exists as a group of eminent scientists, assembled under the auspices of the UN, with a remit to coordinate and collate climate-change evidence from around the world. An important historical precedent occurred when, in 2001, a comprehensive report was released (IPCC, 2001a–c); this was, at the time, the most extensive and detailed climate-modelling exercise ever achieved. Since this report, data and evidence have continued to be amassed, resulting in the even more detailed IPCC report in 2007; the latter is currently the most up-to-date evaluation concerning the current state of Earth's changing climate. You might have already discovered this report in Web Activity 1.2, and you will learn more about its details later in the course.

So, what was the IPCC's conclusion in 2001? Basically, it was the same as that of the Asia–Pacific Network for Global Change Research Workshop. The IPCC argued not only that global climate change is occurring, but also that the Earth is warming at a faster rate than was previously expected. It predicted that temperatures could rise by as much as 5.8 °C by the end of the 21st century (IPCC, 2001a, p. 575). But identifying the warming trend was not enough. To substantiate the claim that climate change is a legitimate environmental problem, the IPCC had to agree on the main cause. Its verdict? Human activity was responsible for most of the problem, with industrial pollution, and in particular gas emissions, as the worst offender. Importantly, this conclusion has now been given further credence from the evidence contained in the 2007 IPCC report and, if anything, the effects of global warming may be worse than initially thought.

1.4.1   Contesting the claims

Certainly, climate change looks like very bad news for people on low-lying islands. Accordingly, having a large international panel of scientists to substantiate the claim of global warming would seem to ensure world opinion would be on the side of the Maldivian and other islanders. Unfortunately, finding supporting scientific evidence is rarely this simple. There are many people and groups around the world, for instance the Lavoisier Group in Australia, who remain sceptical about the link between climate change and human activities, and they too have high calibre scientists to back their claims.

Earlier, doubters tended to discount climate change altogether, and there were always some scientists prepared to argue that climate had not changed significantly over recent centuries. However, the more recent sceptics are willing to admit that climate change is occurring, but are not satisfied that human activity is the main cause. Statistician Björn Lomborg, writing in 2001, conceded that 'the temperature of the late twentieth century is greater than in many previous centuries'. But he went on to state, 'this cannot be taken as a simple indication of overwhelming global warming as we are also coming out of a Little Ice Age' (Lomborg, 2001, p. 263).

Lomborg suggested that the currently observed patterns of warming had more to do with naturally occurring long-term fluctuations than they did with human activity. Other scientists have argued that changes in energy output from the Sun, or else changes in the pattern of the Earth's orbit, are the more likely culprits for global warming. Whatever people want to make of such claims, these sceptics do raise a very important point: there is no simple baseline against which we can measure 'deviation' of global temperature from 'normal'. The Earth's temperature fluctuates according to rhythms with different timescales, including daily temperature cycles and the annual rhythm of the seasons. In addition, there are other rhythms that occur over even longer timescales, from decades up to tens or even hundreds of millennia (the so-called **Milankovitch cycles**), which are now known to influence or control glacial and interglacial cycles (Hays et al., 1976; Zachos et al., 2001).

Trying to ascertain whether the planet's climate is showing an increase in extreme weather events is also another question that comes up against the 'background noise' of the Earth's natural variability. It has been argued that parts of the world are becoming prone to more intense storms, and that the frequency and intensity of floods, droughts and fires caused by dryness is rising. Once again, the question arises of just what exactly constitutes a 'normal' storm, or an 'ordinary' rainy season. In recognition of this problem, the 2001 IPCC report conceded that observational data was not yet complete or reliable enough to show *any* global trends over the past 50 years. The best it could say was that its models suggest that increases in high wind speeds and extremes of rainfall are 'likely over some areas' (IPCC, 2001a, Table 9.6, p. 575).

So how do we know that the documented trends have more to do with the contributions of human beings than with the normal variation of global temperature? So far in this book, the evidence has not been examined in enough depth to make an informed judgement. What can be pointed out is that the scientists involved in the Asia–Pacific workshop and the 2001 IPCC were already fully aware of this background of naturally occurring fluctuations, and had already taken them into account in their calculations of the human contribution to climate change. Importantly, with regard to some, but not all, observations of climatic variation, they were still confident about distinguishing human impacts from 'naturally occurring' fluctuations.

1.4.2   Hard evidence, shaky ground

If determining climate change is complicated, surely measuring sea level is simpler? There might be high tides and low tides, but shouldn't we be able to tell if the highest tides are getting higher? The raising of sea level is one of the most feared aspects of global warming for inhabitants of the low-lying parts of the planet. Heating expands the volume of water, and global warming would be expected to result in a rise in the level of the planet's seas and oceans – estimated at about 1 metre (m) for every 1 °C increase in global mean sea temperature. At the same time, the melting of glaciers is also adding water to overall sea level (Figure 1.10). It is estimated that global sea levels would rise by about 5 m if the entire Greenland ice sheet melted, and by a huge 60 to 70 m if all of the Antarctic ice melted!

Figure 1.10   An Antarctic glacier calving icebergs into the sea.

Environmental activists argue that climate-induced sea-level change is already under way. For example, Greenpeace claims that two islets in the Kiribati archipelago in the West Pacific have already disappeared. As you probably guessed from the discussion above, sceptics can attribute these observed changes to the natural fluctuations in the Earth's climate – attributing them to those documented warming occurring mechanisms that occur independently of human influence.

However, both IPCC reports take into account this 'background rate' in their modelling of sea-level change. The current estimate is of a sea-level rise of about 5 mm per year: that is, between two and four times higher than the rate in the past 100 years (estimated at 1.0–2.5 mm per year). However, the complexity of the models means that predictions for the future cover a large range of possibilities. In the 2001 report, the maximum prediction was an increase of 88 cm by the year 2100, while the minimum estimate is 9 cm (IPCC, 2001a, p. 16). These values gives a middle range around 50 cm. The 2001 IPCC report goes on to detail what this would mean for low-lying islands:

> Many small island nations are only a few meters above present sea-level. These states may face serious threat of permanent inundation from sea-level rise. Among the most vulnerable of these island states are the Marshall Islands, Kiribati, Tuvalu, Tonga, the Federated States of Micronesia, and the Cook Islands (in the Pacific Ocean); Antigua and Nevis (in the Caribbean Sea); and the Maldives (in the Indian Ocean).

> (IPCC, 2001b)

Or, to be more specific:

> An 80-cm sea-level rise could inundate two-thirds of the Marshall Islands and Kiribati.

> A 90-cm sea-level rise could cause 85% of Male, the capital of the Maldives, to be inundated.

> (IPCC, 2001b)

Does the evidence support the predictions of the model, so far? Even given the range covered by the IPCC, there are scientists who believe there is no evidence of observable acceleration of sea-level rise. That is, none beyond that which could be expected to result from natural climatic variability. Scientists from the National Tidal Facility (NTF) of Flinders University, South Australia have shown that over the past 25 years there has been no change in average sea level. As the NTF Director Dr Wolfgang Scherer put it: 'There is no acceleration in sea-level rise – none that we can discern, at all' (Amos, 2000).

So far, this chapter is neither trying to prove nor disprove claims about global climate change. Instead, the intention is to demonstrate that 'proof' of the existence of environmental change, using seemingly straightforward measurements, can often be very contentious. For complex issues such as global climate change, where numerous variables are involved, there are many opportunities for scientists to take issue with their colleagues' findings, and to provide conflicting interpretations of available data. They can also disagree about the procedures for gathering data, the completeness or coverage of data, the ways in which the data are analysed and then, finally, the conclusions that are made. Perhaps most importantly, and fundamentally, they can take issue with the assumptions on which entire research programmes are based. The theoretical framework that shapes a particular programme of research is often an area of contention equal to the arguments over the quality of data gathered; this is because it is the 'framework' that helps decide the kind of questions that will be addressed during the work.

Such contention does not make science any less important to the understanding of the environmental issues. In a way, it is the very fact that different researchers are constantly taking each other to task that gives us confidence when the majority of the scientific community finally arrives at consensus. However, consensus doesn't mean that the conclusions are final and will be accepted for all time. But at least if we know that an idea or a theory has been rigorously argued over before being accepted, it has probably had a thorough critical appraisal and thus represents the best interpretation available at the time.

But these are not the only potential sources of variation. You have seen that some scientists argue that observable changes in sea level can be attributed to the varying temperatures that are part of the normal variance of the planet's climate. As if this is not complicated enough already, there is another potential source of concern among scientists who are trying to monitor sea level – the land itself can move!

Although the idea of drifting continents was developed in the early 20th century by the eminent polar explorer Alfred Wegener (1880–1930), it was not until the 1960s that scientists finally demonstrated his theory by identifying the processes that cause land masses to move both relative to each other and relative to the ocean basins between them. This became known as the theory of **plate tectonics**. In addition, geologists had also found that the elevation of whole areas of continents can change: in much the same way as a raft will settle lower in the water or bob upwards when someone climbs on or off it, continental land masses may be depressed or allowed to rise upwards by changing the loads on them. For instance, erosion of mountain chains or the melting of thick ice sheets will reduce continental loading resulting in uplift; the deposition of sediments, eruption of thick lava piles, or the development of glaciers and ice sheets will increase the load upon a continent, so causing subsidence. This type of movement is called **isostasy** or 'isostatic adjustment'.

During the last ice age, large areas of the continents were covered in ice – this made them lower relative to other areas unaffected by ice. At the end of the ice ages, when the ice melted, the continental areas that had been affected slowly began to rise back towards their pre-glacial positions – in much the same way as a raft does in the example above. The last ice age to affect the North American and Eurasian continents peaked at about 20 000 years ago and, in Britain, regions of Scotland are still rising a few millimetres a year after the melting – or deglaciation – of its last covering of ice which ended 10 000 years ago. However, during this last glacial period, the south of England was unaffected by the ice sheets so it did not rise; instead, parts were submerged through a rise in sea level caused by the water added to the oceans from the ice melting elsewhere.

With these factors in mind, you can see why it may be difficult to distinguish rising seas from sinking lands. As the scientist Wolfgang Scherer put it in a BBC interview:

> for us, the major uncertainty is land movement. All the historical records of sea-level measure only relative sea-level. If you have a land-mass that is rising, it will look like a lowering of sea-level. Inversely, if the land is sinking, it looks like the sea is rising. And if we are making the linkage to climate, it is the absolute sea-level that is important …

> (Amos, 2000)

So, if continents move, what about small islands? Aside from coral atolls – which are built up from the once-living bodies of small marine organisms – other oceanic islands can be formed as a result of volcanic activity (e.g. the Hawaiian island chain in the Pacific Ocean) or by upheaval of sediment caught in the zones where continental plates collide (e.g. the Andaman Islands in the Indian Ocean). To make matters even more complex, a lowering of sea level, or increased deposition at a particular locality, can allow areas of sea floor to emerge, thus creating new islands!

Of course, there are other stories and viewpoints which continue to claim climate change is the main culprit: for instance, the recent experiences of seawater inundation affecting the Tuvalu islanders in the South Pacific. The people of these small islands are now convinced that their delicate island environment is suffering seriously from an inexorable recent rise in sea level caused by modern global warming (Field, 2002; Shukman, 2008).

Clearly, whatever their origin, the histories of small islands are more turbulent and unstable than those of the continental areas. Whether talking about biological processes that build coral islands, or the geological processes that forge 'rocky' islands, these processes are part of the natural 'rhythm' of the planet which continues to operate long after human beings and other land-based species have made an island their home. As a final chapter in their histories, the long-term fate of small islands is commonly to subside, or to be worn down by the forces of wave and wind and gradually washed away over the millennia, eventually to disappear beneath the waves from which they once arose.

You should now complete the activity associated with this chapter, if you didn't do it earlier.

1.4.3   The challenge of uncertainty

The previous sections looked at the way bold statements about the current and future state of the planet usually turn out to be less clear cut or certain when all the factors involved are considered more closely. This is where **uncertainty** comes in: the third course theme.

From the previous discussion, you should now recognise that uncertainty constantly intrudes on the understanding of environmental problems and the search for solutions. Some of this uncertainty is due to the incompleteness of current knowledge, and it is to be expected that this type of uncertainty might well give way to greater confidence at some time in the future, when more data are available. As you have seen, enormous effort is now going into gathering, processing and analysing information about the state of the planet's climatic systems, all with the aim of reducing uncertainty.

But not all uncertainty can be overcome by better data, or by debates about the best way to interpret this data. Some forms of uncertainty arise because many events or processes simply do not unfold in a predictable way. This is the case where many different factors are involved, each influencing the others in such a way that the outcome is genuinely novel: in other words, an outcome that cannot be predicted on account of what was observed in the past. This sort of uncertainty occurs at the small, everyday level. For example, think of the difficulty of predicting the exact outcome of a sports match or a casual conversation! This can also be the case on a much larger scale, such as most of the major environmental problems which involve a unique coming together of a range of factors and circumstances.

This means that uncertainty is unavoidable: it is both part of the world and part of our understanding of the world. Nevertheless, uncertainty should not prevent us from making decisions about environmental problems. What is vital is to be clear and honest about both the strengths and the limitations of our knowledge claims. Box 1.1 describes how the 2001 IPCC deals with uncertainty.

Box 1.1 How the 2001 IPCC addresses uncertainty

The 2001 IPCC indicates the degree of confidence or uncertainty it has in its conclusions by dividing its findings into four main categories (IPCC, 2001c, p. 24):

Well-established: models incorporate known processes; observations are consistent with models; or multiple lines of evidence support the finding.

Established but incomplete: models incorporate most known processes, although some parameters may not be well tested; observations are somewhat consistent but incomplete; current empirical estimates are well founded, but the possibility of changes in governing processes over time is considerable; or only one or a few lines of evidence support the finding.

Competing explanations: different model representations account for different aspects of observations or evidence or incorporate different aspects of key processes, leading to competing explanations.

Speculative: conceptually plausible ideas that have not received much attention in the literature or are laced with uncertainty that is difficult to reduce.

You will hear more about the different types and degrees of uncertainty during the course, and you will find out more about the implications of uncertainty for different areas of environmental decision making. For now, the discussion turns to one of the major uncertainties that currently haunts the issue of global climate change.

You might recall that both newspaper articles on the Maldives refer to the melting of the ice in Antarctica. For climate-change scientists, the issue here is the possible collapse of a region of the southern polar ice cap called the West

Antarctic Ice Sheet (WAIS) (Figure 1.11). If the WAIS collapsed, it would result in a rise in global sea level of some 5 m over a very short timespan. There is evidence to suggest that it has broken up previously, long before human impact could ever have played a part. It is not yet fully understood why this happened, although researchers recognise that it was triggered by a complex interaction between the various components of the Earth's climate system. Even if a previous collapse of the WAIS could be explained, it would not necessarily give a clear understanding of the present predicament. This is because it is a hugely complex system, in which it is very difficult to isolate or predict the effects of different factors. Most crucially, the fact that human-induced impacts now comprise a whole new set of variables only makes prediction based on past experience even more difficult. The concept of catastrophic change is introduced in Box 1.2, which you should read now.

Figure 1.11   Part of the West Antarctic Ice Sheet (WAIS).

Box 1.2 Understanding a collapse or 'catastrophic' change

When climate-change scientists talk about a 'collapse' in the WAIS, they mean a rapid change from one state to another. Such changes occur in many systems, of various kinds. These are sometimes called **catastrophic changes**, as it is very difficult, or impossible, for the system to return to the original state.

Sometimes a system responds to changes, gradually and step by step, as shown by the ball bearing on a table in Figure 1.12. If you gave the ball bearing a small push, it would roll a short way and then stop. This is the gradual change in the ball bearing 'system'.

Figure 1.12   A ball bearing on a flat table.

However, sometimes you can keep giving the ball bearing small pushes and it comes to a steep drop (Figure 1.13). If you nudge the ball bearing 'over the edge', it gathers momentum until it hits the floor. The drop is rapid and very hard to reverse.

Figure 1.13   A ball bearing going over a steep drop on a table.

In this scenario, the ball bearing system has two 'stable' states. One stable state is composed of the range of movements on the table top. This state is lost once the ball bearing goes over the edge. When it reaches the floor, the system enters an alternative 'stable state', which is composed of the range of movements at this lower level. The system is said to have 'collapsed', or undergone a 'catastrophic' change. Here 'catastrophic' means a sudden, decisive, and often irreversible, change. Such changes are not necessarily bad for humans and happen on various scales all around us and all the time.

Although the ball bearing is a very simple example, many systems in the natural and the social world are now known to change in this way. For example, the WAIS appears to be part of system that has two stable states – the ice sheet there and the ice sheet gone. The question is when and what is the likelihood of the 'drop'? Pressures leading to a transformation might be building up, but there are often no visible signs that a shift is coming (the drop in Figure 1.13).

So what are the chances that human-induced climate change might be pushing the WAIS towards collapse? The best that the 2001 IPCC could suggest was a 'low-to-medium confidence' prediction that rapid and large temperature increases would result in a large-scale collapse, although it has concluded that this collapse is very unlikely to happen over the next century. This finding comes under the 'Established but incomplete' category of Box 1.1. However, such a respite does not absolve today's heavy energy users of responsibility. In the case of the WAIS, as with many systems prone to catastrophic changes, there may be a considerable time lag between the pressures building up to a change and the change occurring.

The 2001 IPCC points out that current human contributions to climate change might not be fully felt in Antarctica for centuries, or even millennia.

1.5   Sustainability in a dynamic world

As you saw earlier in this chapter, there is a tendency to think about islands as 'paradises', or pristine, undisturbed places. To think about islands, or any other sort of landscape, in this way implies that everything was perfect in the beginning. But islands often have turbulent beginnings, and continue to be shaped and changed by dynamic processes throughout their existence (Figure 1.14). This is the case, to varying degrees, for all landforms, both insular and continental.

Figure 1.14   An island formed by volcanic activity: steam and volcanic gas clouds over White Island, New Zealand.

The dynamism of the natural world means that there is no state of perfection – no stable baseline against which to measure human-induced changes. It also means that it is often extremely difficult to distinguish human-induced or **anthropogenic** changes from the background of ongoing variation and change. Even on a relatively brief timescale – such as a normal day and night – there are changes in temperature and light, and in the activity of living organisms. On a much longer timescale, land masses buckle and shift, great plates of ice advance and retreat, and the oceans rise and fall. In the extreme long term, stars eventually burn out and die.

What does this mean for the ideal of sustainability? As you saw in Section 1.2, sustainability is about living without undermining the conditions, processes and resources that support life. So how can we tell if our demands on the physical and living systems we rely on are too great? In the short term, we often seem to get away with quite extravagant demands on natural systems. But because of the way in which changes of state occur in systems, this may simply mean that the eventual effects are not yet visible. In the long term, as the saying goes, we are all dead. Even without human impacts, changes in the physical systems that all life relies on will eventually render life, as we know it, unsustainable.

This means that timescales are crucial when considering sustainability. The implication of inhabiting a world with many different rhythms of change and variance is that human impacts must always be addressed in a context of other forces and processes, many of which operate on scales that greatly exceed our everyday 'commonsense' perceptions.

One of the great challenges that environmentalists face is to disentangle human-induced change from natural processes, and to identify the sources of these anthropogenic transformations. In this regard, as you have seen, scientific evidence plays a vital role. But, at the same time, the complex interplay of many dynamic processes means that, even with massive investments in research, there will always be uncertainties. However, it is one thing to acknowledge uncertainty and quite another to live in the light of this knowledge. Taking uncertainty into consideration – working with it, through it and around it – is a central part of the environmental challenge.

Uncertainty raises important questions for the concept of sustainability. What exactly are we trying to 'sustain' in a world that both gives and takes away resources for living in great sweeping motions of its own? What sort of goals should we choose to develop or progress towards, once we have become aware that the goalposts are bound to shift, or that the whole playing field might tilt or crumple? Whatever course of action is chosen, we can be assured that new challenges will always arise. This is one reason why you should be deeply suspicious of any 'final solutions' to long-term environmental issues or to the broader question of how human beings should best interact with the rest of the natural world.

The variability of the planet, and the uncertainty that goes with it, means that all people, wherever they live, are to some degree vulnerable to changes in their environment. Human disturbance tends to add to this vulnerability – often making already vulnerable people much more so. As the precarious situation of the Maldivian islanders and others living in low-lying areas makes clear, vulnerability is not evenly shared.

While the risk of inundation may be an extreme case, it highlights two crucial issues. The first is the need for those who are most vulnerable to have a strong say in world affairs. So far, the importance of 'expert knowledge' has been emphasised to inform the environmental decision-making process – especially where knowledge is needed that exceeds our 'common senses'. However, science can only help us with certain aspects of environmental problems. There are other forms of experience and ways of knowing that are also vital. One reason for considering global environmental changes from the point of view of island people was to make it clear that there are different perspectives on environmental problems, and that different groups of people bring differing interests, values and experiences to the debating table.

The second issue, which is related to the first, is the question of responsibility. As the concept of globalisation suggests, the things we do in our own, local part of the world can impact on the far side of the globe, and vice versa. In the case of global climate changes, you have seen that many of the most vulnerable people are paying the price for changes that are not of their own making – while others reap the benefits. This inequity raises the issue of how those who have triggered environmental changes should face the question of their responsibility for the lives of other people – others who may be distant in either space or time.

You will engage with these issues throughout the course. Before facing them head on, however, you need to know more about the dynamics of the planet, and what they mean for human beings – for the social and cultural life of our species. In the next two chapters, you will look more closely at the interface between the living planet and the social world; starting from small-scale, localised cases and building up towards the global scale.

1.6   Summary of Chapter 1

1.1   Environmental problems are an important aspect of globalisation – a concept that refers to the process and the experience of the increasing interconnectedness of the world.

1.2   Sustainability has emerged as a central issue of contemporary environmentalism in response to the charge that continued economic growth is undermining the long-term life-support systems of the planet.

1.3   The claim that less-developed nations have a right to benefit from economic growth in the same way that developed nations have in the past presents a serious challenge for advocates of sustainability.

1.4   'Sustainable development' makes an explicit connection between environmental issues and issues of global economic inequality. The concept suggests that it is possible to reconcile further social and economic development with environmental protection.

1.5   Mounting evidence about human-induced environmental change on a global scale is a cogent reminder that there is a continuing tension between calls for continued economic growth and environmental sustainability.

1.6   The predicament of people living on small islands and in other low-lying areas demonstrates that vulnerability to global environmental changes is not evenly distributed. This inequity raises important ethical and political issues about the responsibility of people elsewhere in the world for these threats.

1.7   In the modern world, claims about environmental risk and degradation must be backed up by scientific evidence.

1.8   Most of the major claims about human-induced global environmental change are contested to some degree, although there is an emerging consensus over some of the major points.

1.9   One of the main sources of contention is how the distinction should be made between human-induced changes and changes caused by natural variation – such as fluctuations of climate or sea level and geological instability.

1.10   An added difficulty with tracking the impact of human activities arises because of the patterns of stability of many of the physical and biological systems in question. Systems may reach a threshold and change their state quite suddenly, so it can be difficult to gauge the human contribution to change or to predict when a change of state might occur.

1.11   There are many uncertainties in the state of knowledge about environmental change, both because of inadequacies of the available data and analysis, and because of the inherent unpredictability of some of the systems that are being studied. This means that there will always be a play-off between confidence and uncertainty.

1.12   A sense of the dynamism and turbulence that is part of the natural world itself increasingly forms the backdrop to the sustainability issue – raising questions about what we are trying to sustain and how the goals of development should be set.

Questions for Chapter I

Question 1.1

From what you have read in this chapter, which of the following, if any, are useful lessons we should take from the concept of globalisation?

(a) Increasing global interconnectivity entails risks as well as opportunities.

(b) Increasing global interconnectivity will make the world a better place.

(c) Today, we are all in the same situation.

(d) The benefits and costs of most forms of global interconnectivity are not evenly shared.

(e) The internet makes all other media obsolete.

Question 1.2

Explain, in a couple of sentences, why it might be a good idea to place limits on the number of tourists who visit a small island each year.

Question 1.3

Which of the following demands, if any, is the concept of sustainable development intended to satisfy?

(a) The less-developed world should be able to share the standard of living of the wealthiest countries.

(b) The developed world should abandon all further economic growth.

(c) The developed world should lower its standard of living until the less-developed world catches up.

(d) Future generations should have access to the same environmental resources and opportunities as present generations.

Question 1.4

In a maximum of 100 words, compare and contrast the way in which someone living in the British Isles and a Maldivian islander might view the prospect of a slight global warming.

Question 1.5

Give two examples of the negative effects of rising sea level on low-lying islands such as the Maldives.

Question 1.6

In a maximum of 100 words, explain why measurements showing steady increases in temperature taken over 10 years on a small island would be insufficient proof of human-induced global warming.

Question 1.7

Which of the following statements, if any, could conceivably explain an observed increase in sea level?

(a) The sea has increased in volume through human-induced global warming.

(b) The sea has increased in volume through warming caused by long-term natural fluctuations.

(c) The sea level has risen because human-induced warming has caused glaciers to melt.

(d) The sea level has risen because deglaciation has caused glaciers to melt.

(e) Land areas have risen isostatically through the after-effects of glaciation.

(f) Land areas originally covered by an ice sheet have subsided after the melting of that ice.

(g) Land areas have been generated by tectonic activity.

Question 1.8

List three factors that could explain how a new tropical oceanic island has come into being.

Question 1.9

Which of the following statements, if any, suggest a *mis*understanding of the implications of uncertainty in the field of environmental change?

(a) Improved data will generally reduce uncertainty.

(b) Much-improved data will eliminate uncertainty.

(c) We can avoid the drawbacks of uncertainty if we remember that there is nothing new under the Sun.

(d) A high degree of uncertainty is associated with genuinely novel events.

(e) The presence of uncertainty prevents effective environmental decision making.

(f) The presence of uncertainty should make us suspicious of 'final' and absolute solutions to environmental problems.

Question 1.10

Which of the following statements, if any, are true about 'catastrophic' changes in the state of a system?

(a) They are difficult to reverse or undo.

(b) They always have disastrous effects on human beings.

(c) There are many warning signs that a change is on the way.

(d) In normal circumstances, systems with two alternative states are finely balanced between these states.

(e) They are a major source of uncertainty.

References

Amos, J. (2000) '"No Acceleration' in Pacific Sea Rise', BBC News Online: http://news.bbc.co.uk/1/hi/sci/tech/1035489.stm (Accessed 21 November 2008).

Field, M. (2002) 'Global warming not sinking Tuvalu – but maybe its own people are' [online], http://nzclimatescience.net/index.php?option=com_content&task=view&id=14&Itemid=1 (Accessed 21 November 2008).

French, H. (2000) *Vanishing Borders: Protecting the Planet in the Age of Globalization*, New York, Norton.

Hays, J.D., Imbrie, J. and Shackleton, N.J. (1976) 'Variations in the Earth's orbit: pacemaker of the ice ages', *Science*, vol. 194, no. 4270, pp. 1121–32. Available online at: www.sciencemag.org/cgi/content/abstract/194/4270/1121 (Accessed 2 February 2009).

Independent Commission on International Development Issues (1980) *North, South: A Programme for Survival*, London, Pan. (Also known as the Brandt Report.)

IPCC (2001a) *Climate Change 2001: The Scientific Basis. Contribution of Working Group I to the Third Assessment Report of the Intergovernmental Panel on Climate Change*, Cambridge, Cambridge University Press.

IPCC (2001b) 'Threatened small island states', in *Climate Change 2001: Impacts, Adaptation and Vulnerability* [online], www.grida.no/publications/other/ipcc_tar/?src=/climate/ipcc_tar/wg2/index.htm (Accessed 21 November 2008).

IPCC (2001c) *Climate Change 2001: Impacts, Adaptation and Vulnerability. Contribution of Working Group II to the Third Assessment Report of the Intergovernmental Panel on Climate Change*, Cambridge, Cambridge University Press.

Lomborg, B. (2001) *The Skeptical Environmentalist: Measuring the Real State of the World*, Cambridge, Cambridge University Press.

Palm Beach, Maldives (1997) [online], http://palmbeach-maldives.com/island.htm (Accessed 20 November 2008).

Shukman, D. (2008) 'Tuvalu Struggles to Hold Back Tide', BBC News Online, http://news.bbc.co.uk/1/hi/sci/tech/7203313.stm (Accessed 21 November 2008).

World Commission on Environment and Development (WCED) (1987) *Our Common Future*, Oxford, Oxford University Press. (Also known as the Brundtland Report.)

Zachos, J., Pagani, M., Sloan, L., Thomas, E. and Billups, K. (2001) 'Trends, rhythms, and aberrations in global climate 65 Ma to present', *Science*, vol. 292, no. 5517, pp. 686–93. Available online at www.sciencemag.org/cgi/content/abstract/292/5517/686 (Accessed 4 February 2009).

Chapter 2
Island life: adventures in isolation and openness

2.1   Introduction

So far this book has looked at the geological and climatic transformations that make and remake islands. In focusing on these powerful physical forces not much has been said about another force that shapes the planet – life itself. While life on Earth may seem dwarfed by the vastness of rock, water and air, it has been calculated that the total mass of all the organisms that have ever lived is somewhere between 1000 and 10 000 times the mass of the Earth itself (Rampino and Caldeira, 1994, p. 103).

For all that living creatures are diverse and fascinating in themselves, if our concern is environmental issues, ecosystems will be of most interest to us. The World Resources Institute defines an **ecosystem** as 'a community of interacting organisms and the physical environment they live in' (WRI, 2000, p. 10). Ecosystems can be any size: they can be as small as a pond in a garden, or as large as an ocean. Each ecosystem tends to blend into its neighbours and form part of larger ecosystems, expanding up to the level of the entire planet.

What makes an ecosystem distinct is a certain integrity that comes from the degree of interconnectivity between its parts. At the same time, every ecosystem relies on energy from the outside and on exchanges of organic and inorganic matter with surrounding ecosystems. Human beings have a somewhat ambivalent place in ecosystems. We are part of the ecosystems we live in but we also have our own systems. Our 'social systems' have their own integrity and dynamics and, of course, their own exchanges with other social systems.

This chapter looks at the interplay between life and landform, and between human beings and other forms of life. Islands are a good model because they have distinct boundaries: it is easier to see the exchanges than in ecosystems on larger land masses. In many cases we also have a fairly clear idea of when human beings first arrived on previously uninhabited islands. This gives us a picture of what happens when groups of people encounter ecosystems when neither is accustomed to the other.

The journeys and migrations that first brought human beings to oceanic islands are the predecessors of today's globalisation. This chapter tracks some cases of human mobility that will take you around the planet and back in history, starting with the early European exploration of the world's oceans, then heading back still further in time.

The evidence about human arrival on islands tells a story of the extreme vulnerability of island ecosystems. But the study of island life also demonstrates that islands are sites where life's creativity can be observed with particular clarity (Figure 2.1). 'Island life', in this sense, shows how vulnerability and change are two sides of the same coin. However, it is not only biological life that adapts and

Figure 2.1   Island ecosystems: water plants and lowland forest at Waimea Falls, Oahu, Hawaii.

evolves. You will also see that human settlers on islands must adapt their social lives if they too are to survive in the long term. This chapter describes the challenges that a new environment places on human social life and starts to look at the ways societies steer or 'govern' their way through these challenges.

2.2   Tropical island paradises

From around the 14th century onwards, European people set out on a phase of wide ranging maritime exploration. However, they were not the first people to make long voyages. With one notable exception (which you will learn more about later in this book), all of the world's large land masses had already been settled and very many small islands had been visited or colonised. But there were still 'unknown' islands, and these came to play an important strategic role in European expansion.

When European mariners first landed on fertile and uninhabited islands in the middle of the oceans – such as St Helena, Cape Verde, the Azores and the Madeiras in the Atlantic Ocean, and Mauritius in the Indian Ocean (Figure 2.2) – it must have seemed to them like divine providence. As a Dutch voyager described St Helena in 1589:

> The water is excellently good and falleth down from the mountains and so runneth in great abundance by small channels to the sea … that it seemed a wonder wrought by God … it is an earthly paradise for the Portuguese ships and seemeth to have been miraculously discovered for the refreshing and servicing of the same, considering the smallness and highness of the land, lying in the middle of the Ocean seas …

> (cited in Grove, 1995, p. 98)

Figure 2.2   Islands of the Atlantic and Indian Oceans (inset: St Helena).

Activity 2.1   Island stopovers

Imagine you are a ship's crew member in the 17th century, coming across an island in the middle of an arduous voyage. Remember, seafarers went for months without fresh food, and diseases such as scurvy (caused by vitamin C deficiency) were the bane of long voyages. In the best of all possible worlds, what would you hope to gain from an island stopover? Write down a few ideas.

Comment

Now compare your notes with the account of St Helena provided by J. A. von Mandelslo, a 17th-century traveller from Holstein (now in Germany) on his way to India:

> At this place a man may at any time of the year [find] figs and pomegranates; citrus and oranges are there, also goats … barbary hens, pheasants, partridges, quails, peacocks, pigeons; and great stocks of all sorts of birds, as also salt for the keeping of them, so that ships may be sufficiently provided with all things if they would stay there any time. The sea supplies with more fish than can be consumed, and the earth brings forth so many excellent herbs, that the Portuguez, unwilling to retard their voyage, leave at this place their sick men, who recover their health within a few days and having only a little Oyl, rice byskets and spice, make a shift to live there till the ships come hither next year.

> (cited in Grove, 1995, p. 43, spelling as in original)

As well as some of the points noted by this 17th-century voyager, you might have mentioned others. Like sex, for example. Sexual liaisons were clearly not a feature of uninhabited islands but they were certainly a major attraction for early European visitors to some Pacific islands.

Tales of lush, verdant islands thrilled sailors and armchair travellers alike – not only for their practical value but also because these 'enchanted isles' reminded these people of the biblical 'Eden'. You might have noticed that some of the trees and animals in the account above (as the writer was aware) had been brought in by earlier visitors:

> the few trees they planted and the little stock of cattle they left there hath so furnished it that it is … sufficient to refresh all the fleets that come hither.

> (cited in Grove, 1995, p. 43)

The unexpected thriving of these unattended introduced species bolstered the association of oceanic islands with an 'earthly paradise'. From using the islands as provisioning stops, it was not long before European visitors established permanent settlements (Figure 2.3).

On these islands European settlers first experimented with plantation agriculture. In an important sense, these trial runs in colonisation prepared the way for the coming age of imperialism. But as permanent settlement progressed, the idea of

Figure 2.3   A late 16th-century print of Dutch colonists on Mauritius in the Indian Ocean.

33

fertile and paradise-like islands took a serious blow. In a few decades, or even less, settlers began to notice that their activities were having seriously damaging effects on the environment of the islands that were so crucial to their maritime ventures.

Some of the first problems documented were the effects of deforestation. A visiting French scientist reported of 18th-century Mauritius:

> Reckless and ignorant men, thinking of nothing but themselves, have ravaged the island, destroying the trees by fire to make a fortune for themselves at the expense of the colony, leaving nothing for their successors but arid lands abandoned by rain and exposed without relief to storms and the burning sun.

> (cited in Grove, 1995, p. 202)

Island inhabitants observed the effect of clearing forests on soil cover. The official 18th-century records of St Helena noted that 'the weather breaks and washes away the soil till the naked rocks appear' (cited in Grove, 1995, p. 121). This eroding soil then silted up rivers and harbours and contaminated water supplies. Not surprisingly, being surrounded by thousands of miles of salty ocean, any threat to an island's freshwater supply was a vital issue. Very early on, informed observers seriously considered the idea that deforestation had a deleterious effect on mist and rainfall, and hence on water supplies. By the mid-18th century, theories about human-induced climate change were widespread among island administrators, and it was broadly accepted that deforestation posed a serious threat to the whole colonial project.

2.3   Threats to island life

European settlers on oceanic islands were learning a hard lesson about *unsustainable* development. However, it was not only concern with climate change and deforestation that came early to these small islands – the first settlers and visitors began to develop a basic, hands-on understanding of their impact on the biological life of islands. At least half a century before Charles Darwin sailed on HMS *Beagle* (1832–6), which led to his valuable insights on the origins of species on the Galápagos Islands, colonial scientists on islands such as Mauritius and St Helena had already developed a clear sense of the peculiar qualities of island biota. Equally importantly, they had also recognised its susceptibility to human-induced changes. François Leguat, a member of a French expedition to Mauritius at the end of the 17th century, recounted that 'this island fairly abounded with Wild Geese and Ducks, Moorhens, Quails, Sea and Land Tortoises, but now all these have become scarce' (cited in Grove, 1995, p. 151).

One of the first examples of the vulnerability of island wildlife was the infamous case of the dodo (Figure 2.4). This large, flightless bird was **endemic** to Mauritius – in other words, it was found there and nowhere else. Adapted to life on an island with no human occupants or terrestrial mammals, dodos had little need for 'fight or flight' and, when faced with new threats, their behaviour tended to be incautious or naive. It was also a ground-nesting species, laying a single egg per clutch.

However, widespread hunting was not the worst of the dodo's problems. The success of introduced domestic animals may have been a boon to human settlers,

Figure 2.4   An early 17th-century painting of a dodo (*Raphus cucullatus*).

but astute observers soon noted a downside to their extraordinary proliferation. Leguat surmised the main agent of destruction on Mauritius. As he wrote of the pigs that had been introduced to the island: 'these beasts do a great deal of damage to the inhabitants, by devouring all the young animals they catch' (cited in Grove, 1995, p. 151). The problem of the destructive spread of introduced species that Leguat identified is now known as **bioinvasion**. Recent research supports his conclusion but adds a second culprit. A species of monkey from southeast Asia – the crab-eating macaque (*Macaca fascicularis*) – was also introduced (perhaps accidentally) to Mauritius, where it reproduced prolifically. Archaeological evidence suggests that both pigs and monkeys preyed on the eggs and the young of the dodo.

The last eyewitness account of dodos was by Dutch sailors shipwrecked on Mauritius in 1662, only 155 years after the islands were first sighted by European seafarers. Dodos had already vanished from the main island but one was spotted – and subsequently spitted – by the hungry castaways on a small islet off the coast: perhaps just far enough off to hold pigs and monkeys at bay. Presumably, at some moment not long after the sailors were rescued, on a sliver of land probably too small to support a viable population, the last dodo quietly expired (Quammen, 1996).

The dodo became part of the European bestiary of wondrous exotic creatures, where it has been – rather unfairly – characterised as fat, stupid and sluggish. Reports of its extinction had considerable impact, as it was the first time that people in Europe were aware of an animal disappearing off the face of the Earth.

2.4   Lessons from small islands

Aside from the phrase 'as dead as a dodo' and the sorry story it commemorates, it is remarkable how little of the environmental history of Europe's oceanic island colonies has entered today's environmental consciousness – particularly when you consider the common concerns.

■ From the account of European impacts on islands above, how many problems can you recognise that are also contemporary issues? Try to give six examples.

☐ You might have thought of:

deforestation

soil erosion

watershed deterioration and freshwater pollution

climate change

loss of biological diversity, including total extinction

bioinvasion.

Some of these problems are, of course, closely related. The main point is that there are important parallels between the impacts deriving from early European movement around the planet, and the environmental problems associated with the more intensive global movements and exchanges of today's world. The evidence from the settlement of uninhabited islands points to the relationship between global movement and the problem of sustainability. Europeans who settled on small tropical islands were entering environments very different from those they were familiar with at home. This transition meant that the knowledge and the skills they brought with them had a high chance of being unsuited to the places they colonised – thus greatly increasing the risk that the activities they engaged in would be unsustainable in the long term.

Another way of putting this is to say that, at the point of their arrival, European knowledge of tropical islands and their ecosystems was extremely incomplete. This would now be recognised as a case of high uncertainty. But at the time, Europeans tended to be quite confident that their way of doing things was the best of all possible ways, and hence appropriate all over the world. The implication of this was that their levels of confidence often far exceeded the data they had available, resulting in a succession of risky and unsustainable practices. What greatly exacerbated this situation is the fact that many of the vital decisions about island 'improvement' were made back in the centres of European power – at the head offices of merchant companies or the seats of government.

However, over time, some European colonists on small islands became very aware of their mistakes. As you have seen, they observed the changes they were bringing about, and in many cases they changed their behaviour quite markedly. Indeed, environmental historian Richard Grove has argued that an early form of 'environmental' awareness arose out of the experience of the degradation of small island colonies. This resulted in some pioneering legislation in an attempt to mitigate the damage that was being done (Grove, 1995). Just as groups of environmentally conscious people are today attempting to steer their societies away from destructive practices, so too did alliances of island administrators, settlers and visiting scientists attempt to reset the course of the small tropical islands, several centuries ago.

The question of 'steering' societies involves the notion of **governance** – the fourth and final course theme. 'Governance' is a term that refers to all the means by which various people or groups attempt to control, manage or set the course of their societies. The term comes from *kubernetes*, the ancient Greek word for 'helmsman', a reference to the fact that running a society is a bit like keeping a ship on course through shifting winds and swells. 'Government' has the same root but with the connotation of elites or experts managing from above – and sending their directives from 'the top down'. The concept of governance, by contrast, is much more encompassing – taking in all the different 'actors' who can make a difference to the way a society or state is run, all the way from the 'bottom' to the 'top'.

With regard to 'steering' small island colonies, the role of state bodies and boards of company directors far away in the capitals of Europe can be described as a form of govern*ment* – enacted through local representatives on the islands. However, in cases when these local representatives took note of what was happening locally and attempted to set a different course for the island colonies, it might be better to say govern*ance* than govern*ment*. In some cases, local attempts to make island agriculture more sustainable led to disagreement and conflict with directors back at head office. It is important to note that those with experience of events 'on the ground' could often make a difference – helped by the fact that the people 'at the top' were usually a long sea voyage away.

It is also worth noting that voyaging scientists played an important part in the emergence of early environmental sensibilities. Travelling by sea, they could 'network' between one island and another, and in this way provided an alternative flow of information to the top-down flow from European centres to their colonies (Grove, 1995, pp. 74, 137–8). So, while the internet might be very important to environmentalists today, it is not the first 'global network' of environmental data and ideas!

2.5   Environmentalism and the idea of 'paradise'

As Grove points out, the relevance of this early form of 'environmentalism' to the rest of the world was not apparent at the time. He concludes: 'there are very few indications that contemporary observers believed that the kinds of environmental changes observed on oceanic islands could also happen on a continental scale' (Grove, 1995, p. 365). The intervening history of European expansion is complex and messy, and it is difficult to trace a line of descent from early environmental awareness on small islands to the consciousness and activism of today.

However, there is one very significant way in which the experience of tropical islands has been passed on, all the way to the present.

Now is a good time to begin the website activities associated with this chapter.

■ Does the imagery of the early European visitors remind you of anything you have already encountered in this course?

☐ The portrayal of tropical islands as an 'earthly paradise' anticipates the references to the type of undisturbed perfection that features in the Maldives promotional literature and website (Section 1.3).

Activity 2.2   Tropical island paradise?

What are the common features of the earliest and the latest depictions of tropical island paradises? Write down your ideas. See if you can come up with two or three points.

Comment

Ideas of paradise, such as the biblical idea of 'Eden' (Figure 2.5), often use imagery of island habitats which include an extraordinary diversity of living creatures, and such an abundance of the resources for good living that labour is scarcely required (fruit tends to feature prominently for just this reason). The scenario is relaxing, healthy, even curative, and the climate is always pleasant – a sort of 'perpetual spring'. And, of course, people want this world pretty much to themselves: uninhabited islands and the near-deserted beaches of the holiday brochure make a virtue of no competition with other people to enjoy paradise.

Figure 2.5   A painting of the 'Garden of Eden'.

All this ruminating over 'enchanted' islands may seem like a digression from the pressing issues of sustainable development and global poverty. But its significance should not be taken lightly because the idea of 'Eden' or 'paradise' is as deeply embedded in contemporary environmentalism as it is in the historic voyages literature or the modern tourist industry.

Keep in mind that, even five or six centuries ago, there were few remaining vestiges of truly wild or uncultivated land in Europe. Accordingly, uninhabited islands were a taste of what the world could have been like without human intervention. So, islands played a vital role in cementing the view that the ideal landscape was one devoid of human presence. The degradation, and even collapse, of entire island ecosystems after settlement only reinforced the notion that human impact entailed a corruption of the purity and perfection of nature.

Uninhabited oceanic islands were, in effect, the first 'new worlds' encountered by European sailors and so had a huge effect on their imagination. Once the precedent was set that the original state of nature was without visible human impact, explorers and colonists from Europe continued to conceive of all newly discovered worlds as 'virgin' lands. Unfortunately, this was the case even if the lands already had peoples of their own. As Europeans penetrated the American continent, the idea of the undefiled **wilderness** was still further entrenched. As in the case of early oceanic islands, celebrations of human 'improvement' of the landscape were tempered by feelings of loss, and nostalgia for the once-perfect world that was being destroyed. Wherever 'wilderness' was perceived as the ideal state of nature, there was deep discomfort over its defilement. This view was to become a mainstay of modern environmentalism, no less than it was to emerge as a key ingredient of the tourist industry.

This idea of the original perfection of nature and its subsequent corruption by people has a deep emotional appeal, at least in the western world. But is this a useful point of departure for modern environmental issues?

■ Based on the discussion of environmental issues in Chapter 1, what do you think the shortcomings of the undefiled wilderness idea might be?

☐ The natural world is subject to constant change and fluctuation. The perfect wilderness idea suggests a static state where everything is in balance and in its proper, given place. Taking nature's dynamic qualities seriously challenges this sense of harmony, but it does not imply that 'anything goes'.

Of course, there is nothing new about the idea that the natural world is in constant change. Geological change was accepted in the late 18th century. This idea of change was extended to biological life with the rise of evolutionary theory in the mid-19th century. However, geological change and biological evolution were viewed as imperceptibly slow in relation to the dramatic pace at which humans could transform the natural world. In the popular imagination, the contrast between nature's gradualism and humankind's frenetic activity sustained the idea that the natural world was perfectly adjusted – until human tampering nudged it off balance.

As you have seen, this idea of the perfection of islands does not sit well with the knowledge that oceanic islands have, at some stage, been thrust into existence by geological activity. Also, a closer look at the biological life of islands shows the idea that islands were perfect to start with is problematic.

- ■ What do you think is the main problem with the 'earthly paradise' view of island life?

- ☐ Just as human beings had to cross the sea to colonise oceanic islands, so did all other forms of life.

2.6   Islands and the origin of species

Far from starting off as pure or undefiled 'Edens', the reality is that encroachment or invasion by species is an essential part of the making and remaking of island ecosystems. This is a risky business. Relative to the area of oceans, islands are tiny and few, with the challenge of a sea crossing sorting the occasional winners from the vast multitude of losers. If sex is the preferred means of reproduction, the need for a pair, or at least a pregnant female, means the odds of a successful colonisation skyrocket still further.

The year 2009 marked the bicentenary of the birth of Charles Darwin (1809–1882). He is credited with promulgating the theory of evolution on a scientific basis. However, his work began with his fascination about how terrestrial species colonised oceanic islands. Where some scientists had postulated lost 'sea bridges' connecting islands to continents, Darwin argued in *The Origin of Species* in 1859 that fluctuations in sea level could not explain all the distributions of life, and he set to work exploring other possible means of dispersal. For example, Darwin demonstrated that many seeds could germinate after passing through the digestive system of birds and after long spells of immersion in saltwater. He also speculated about the dispersal of seeds in earth stuck to the feet of birds, and about animals rafting on current-borne debris or even on icebergs in colder latitudes (Darwin, 1996, Chapters 11 and 12).

With regard to life, islands can be described as partially open systems. They may be shaped and defined by the sea surrounding them, but the very premise of island life is the occasional breaching of this boundary. Darwin recognised that, although the challenges could be extreme, the populating of islands is not fundamentally different from the dispersion of living organisms anywhere else. Around the planet, the play between geographical openness and closure, and the alternation between connectivity and isolation, is working its effects on living things.

In Darwin's words, 'barriers of any kind, or obstacles to free migration, are related in a close and important manner to the difference between the productions of various regions' (1996, p. 281). Once these barriers are breached – once an organism enters a new environment and cannot easily retrace its steps – interesting things start happening. It is not movement or dispersal alone that makes a difference, but the novel interaction with a new environment that this dispersal opens up. As Darwin put it, 'neither migration nor isolation in themselves can do anything. These principles come into play only by bringing organisms into new relations with each other, and … with the surrounding physical conditions' (1996, p. 284).

In a sense, every ecosystem is an island to which plants, animals and other life forms arrive from other places, from time to time. However, real islands, offer some of the most clear and striking evidence of the interplay between organisms and new environments: evidence that was to play a vital role in the work of Darwin, Alfred Russel Wallace (1823–1913) and other pioneers of evolutionary theory. As Darwin observed on the Galápagos Islands, and Wallace in the Malay Archipelago, island organisms are clearly related to species on the nearest large land masses – but, just as clearly, they have their own unique and distinctive features.

This is because, where a group of islands is relatively isolated from the mainland and sufficiently spaced out to make it difficult – but not impossible – for living organisms to travel between islands, they can become a hotbed of evolutionary change. A rare new arrival on an island from the mainland must survive in the new environment and, if it succeeds, its descendents must adapt to the new conditions and opportunities the island provides, becoming in the process a different species. Then if some members from this new species happen to colonise one of the other islands, they will have to adapt again. After a time, the population will be so different that, even if some individuals manage to get back to the original island, they won't be able to interbreed with their relatives. They have become two different species. In a group of islands, this process can be repeated over and over again, as, very occasionally, colonists move between islands, until a whole variety of related species is formed. This kind of relatively rapid formation and spread of new species through a particular geographic region is called **adaptive radiation**.

Darwin's discovery that each of the various species of mockingbirds – or 'mocking-thrushes' as he called them – came from a different island of the Galápagos group gave him the idea of divergence from a common ancestor. This idea was filled out by his research on Galápagos finches, which have different beaks specialised for different kinds of food. The Galápagos finches, like the mockingbirds, varied between islands. However, unlike the mockingbirds, Darwin also found cases of several different finches inhabiting the same island. Darwin recognised – not at the time he was collecting his specimens, but much later – that differentiation between species of finch on the same island was the result of adaptation to different feeding opportunities.

Darwin's work showed how the different opportunities offered by new environments resulted in clear changes in form and behaviour. As with organisms anywhere, island species tend to become specialised for life in a particular environment, slotting into or taking over a particular role or **niche** in the ecosystem. On the Galápagos Islands (Figure 2.6a), the finches have diversified into vacant niches that on the mainland would be occupied by other groups of birds such as woodpeckers and warblers, and their beak shapes have become specialised to handle the particular type of food that they exploit (Figure 2.6b).

(a)

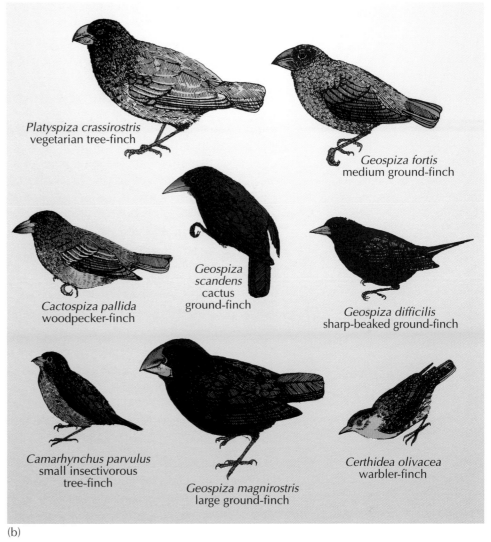

Platyspiza crassirostris
vegetarian tree-finch

Geospiza fortis
medium ground-finch

Cactospiza pallida
woodpecker-finch

Geospiza scandens
cactus
ground-finch

Geospiza difficilis
sharp-beaked ground-finch

Camarhynchus parvulus
small insectivorous
tree-finch

Geospiza magnirostris
large ground-finch

Certhidea olivacea
warbler-finch

(b)

Figure 2.6 (a) The Galápagos Islands in the South Pacific; (b) some of the Galápagos finches, showing variation in beak shape.

However, because of the relative isolation of islands, the processes of specialisation can be especially pronounced. The combination of a restricted habitat and small, isolated populations often gives rise to interesting characteristics. For example, there are often few predators on islands and this can lead to birds losing their dispersal ability: flying uses a lot of energy and when it isn't necessary for survival, birds do better by becoming flightless, as in the case of the dodo and many other island species.

Further, the fact that islands can often support only small populations means that the range of variation in this population is probably also small. If finding an island to be washed up on is a lottery, so too is the sample of genes that the founder population brings with them. Genes contain the basic coding of life, and in sexual reproduction the offspring inherit a composite of genes from both parents. Any rare genes carried by the founder individuals – the sort of genes that would be thinly

41

dispersed among large populations – are likely to be passed on and concentrated in a small interbreeding island population. So, while some of the unique or exaggerated characteristics of island life are clearly adaptations to prevailing environmental conditions, non-adaptive random effects can also play a part.

2.7   The vulnerability of island life

The evolution of life on small islands, as it is everywhere, is a complex process – and it is often difficult to determine precisely why a population of organisms has evolved in that direction. The main point to note is that, far from being in a state of 'original perfection' when the first representatives of the human species wade onshore, island ecosystems are an expression of haphazard arrivals, random effects and ongoing selective pressures. Like any ecosystem, an island is less an example of 'Eden' and more of an open-ended, natural experiment.

This is not the same as saying that island ecosystems have no integrity. Far from it. Every ecosystem comprises a community of interlinked organisms, each with different roles or functions (this is explored in greater detail in Book 2). Which organisms will take which role is not determined in advance but there are, none the less, certain vital functions, or niches, which must be filled in every ecosystem.

Island ecosystems demonstrate that there are recognisable patterns in the assembling of biological communities. Population biologists working in the 1960s identified relationships between the number of species found on islands and island size. This led to new understandings of the carrying capacity of areas of land (i.e. the maximum size of population that can survive and maintain itself there); these insights were then transferred to the study of mainland ecosystems (MacArthur and Wilson, 1963).

The work by population biologists also brought experimental and mathematical evidence to something that had been surmised ever since the early human impacts on previously uninhabited islands such as Mauritius. Namely, that island life has a high level of vulnerability in the face of disturbance. Under conditions of rapid transformation, the evidence suggests, island life has particular difficulty adapting.

Activity 2.3   The dodo's demise

Recalling the dodo's demise, try to pick out the characteristics of *R. cucullatus* that contributed to its lack of resilience (aside from its culinary attractions!). Think of four general points that might be relevant to other species in a similar predicament.

Comment

You might have thought of:

- endemism (i.e. found in only one place)
- limited range and small population base (i.e. a narrow range of genetic variation)
- loss of dispersal ability (i.e. flightless)
- lack of defensive adaptations (naive behaviour).

Put these factors together and you have a general picture of why island species are particularly vulnerable to changes made in their habitat by humans (and by the other life forms that humans bring with them). This shows that the same barriers which channel island species into novel and unique forms also diminish their capacity to adapt to 'stressful' situations. By definition, species found in one small place only are rare, and '[t]o be rare is to have a lower threshold of collective catastrophe' (Quammen, 1996, p. 275).

Islands may be hotspots of biological diversity – or **biodiversity** – but they are also places where biodiversity is most under threat. Just as oceanic islands are susceptible to geological activity, island life is relatively vulnerable to extinction. What counts is the timescale on which processes of transformation are seen. Today there are heated debates about 'background' levels of extinction in relation to the rates of human-induced extinction. One fact that no credible observer can dispute, however, is the extremely high rate at which island species have disappeared.

In the past 400 years, the basic elements of the dodo story have been repeated on numerous occasions. About 171 of the planet's bird species and subspecies are believed to have become extinct (Figure 2.7): 155 of them (about 91%) are from small islands. This number includes 24 species on the Hawaiian Islands and 13 more besides the dodo on Mauritius and the other two islands that comprise the Mascarene Islands. Lord Howe Island, which is a pinprick of land in the sea between Australia and New Zealand, has lost more bird species than Africa, Asia and Europe combined! (Quammen, 1996, p. 264) Island birds have been about 50 times more likely to become extinct than mainland birds – and about 75% of the island extinction has occurred on small islands. The fate of the birds is only a more extreme example of the risks to island life in general.

Figure 2.7   Museum specimens of dodos, surrounded by other extinct birds.

So, as well as teaching us about the origins of new species, islands have also provided most of our knowledge about extinguishing life. The majority of this experience of extinction is directly or indirectly related to European maritime expansion around the globe over the past five or six centuries.

■ What are the three main anthropogenic causes of species extinction?

□ The three main possibilities are:

overexploitation, e.g. hunting or harvesting

habitat damage, e.g. deforestation

bioinvasion.

On islands, each of these human-induced factors exacerbates an already present vulnerability. The direct exploitation of species diminishes the numbers of the already rare ones; habitat destruction increases internal competition; while the introduction of novel species introduces external competition. What makes the problem of bioinvasion particularly deadly is that the type of organism introduced often belongs to classes or genera (groups of species) that would never have crossed the ocean without human assistance.

■ Which invasive genus, not yet mentioned, has a close association with maritime transport and a particularly bad reputation for damaging island ecosystems?

□ Rats – the genus *Rattus*.

The reason for the high number of extinctions already noted on Lord Howe Island is largely rodents. In 1918 a supply ship ran aground and its resident black rats (*Rattus rattus*) got ashore. Within a few years, the rats were responsible for the extinction of at least six endemic bird species.

In many other cases, the direct cause of extinction is not so clear cut. This is because human impacts rarely work alone. Human-induced disturbance weakens the resilience of a species or an ecosystem, eroding its adaptive capacity. But the fatal blow may then be one of the natural perturbations described in Chapter 1: a drought, a cyclone, an erupting volcano or any peak or trough in the normal fluctuations of geoclimatic systems. When this happens, human agents may be left none the wiser about their contribution.

However, as you have seen, colonisers of oceanic islands have learned from experience. So far, this chapter has concentrated on the impact of European explorers and colonists on previously uninhabited islands because this history provides some of the clearest and most recent evidence we have of humans entering a new ecosystem. But uninhabited islands were exceptional, even 600 years ago. The disastrous impact of early European settlers on oceanic islands – and the fact that some important environmental lessons were learned from those disasters – raises some interesting questions. For example, what happens when human settlers have occupied islands for a very long time? Can human social systems and island ecosystems ever adjust fully to one another?

2.8   Island ecosystems and island social systems

When European voyagers first landed on inhabited tropical islands, particularly in the Pacific Ocean, their initial impression was that the islanders were innocent and naive people who lived in blissful harmony with nature.

■ Does this view remind you of anything you have already read in this chapter, and can you see a potential problem with this view?

☐ There is a clear parallel with the early European vision of uninhabited islands as being like 'Eden'. However, like all life on oceanic islands, human beings have to get there. Crossing oceans and colonising new lands does not suggest 'innocence' or 'naivety': it points to high levels of technical skill and social organisation.

During the age of exploration, Europeans imagined a benevolent creator who deposited Pacific islanders on their tropical paradises. In fact, these islanders were descendants of the pioneers of 'blue water' sailing. There is evidence that the first true 'navigators' (people who could sail beyond the sight of land and still find their way home) set out from the peninsulas and closely packed islands of southeast Asia and the East Indies. Known by anthropologists as 'Austronesians', these people mastered the art of long-distance ocean sailing some 3000 to 4000 years ago. They went on to discover and colonise nearly every sizeable Pacific island (Figure 2.8), and settled as far away as Madagascar, in the southwest Indian Ocean. Descendants of Austronesian navigators still inhabit the islands that their ancestors discovered, and many of these islands are the 'tropical paradises' that people in the west love to dream about or visit.

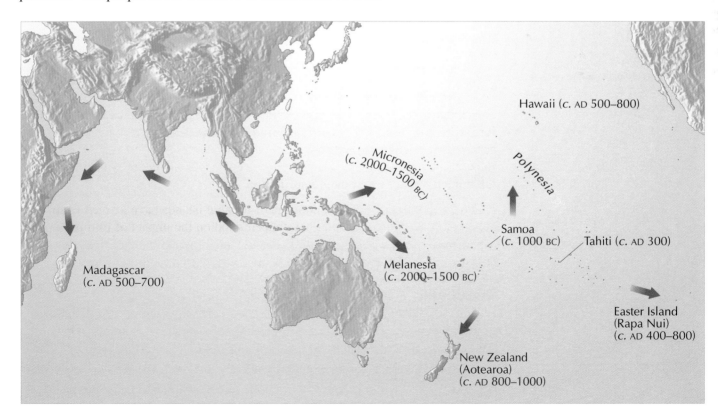

Figure 2.8   The Austronesian diasporas, showing estimated dates of colonisation.

Pacific islands may look pristine to the casual visitor, but all settled lands bear the traces of their inhabitants. One of the transformative forces the first Pacific colonisers brought with them was fire. This was not the occasional fire from a lightning storm or a volcano but a deliberate and regulated anthropogenic burning. Humans have introduced fire almost everywhere they have travelled, using it to clear away old and dense vegetation, and to release nutrients and stimulate new growth. In many cases, the sudden increase in deposits of charcoal in the geological record of islands enables archaeologists to date the arrival of the first human colonists (Pyne, 1997; Fischer, 2002).

Humans also brought their own flora and fauna. 'The surprise, indeed the miracle, of Pacific islands', historian Greg Dening notes, 'is how much of what seems natural to rich and easy South Seas living had to be transported' (1992, p. 308). Very many of the fruits and vegetables that fed migrating islanders – such as breadfruit, taro, plantain, even at times, coconut – were transplanted from island to island, as were the trees they used for building and clothing. So too were the pigs, dogs and chickens they feasted on – which all came from the Asian mainland. The small Pacific rat (*Rattus exulans*) almost always came along too. It was probably a stowaway in many cases, but it was also valued as a food source by some Polynesian people and so may have been deliberately introduced to many islands.

It is the very richness of the biota transported by Pacific islanders in their ocean-going canoes and catamarans (Figure 2.9) that finally convinced western researchers that inter-island migrations were well-planned ventures, rather than accidental, storm-blown occurrences. The long-term viability of the island ecosystems that were at least partly crafted by Pacific seafarers suggests that the species they introduced, and the species endemic to the islands they discovered, have assembled themselves into a functional biological community. But this does not mean the establishment of humans and all their cultural and biotic baggage on a previously unsettled island was a congenial business. In fact, there is much evidence to suggest that the colonisation of the Pacific islands by the ancestors of today's Polynesian people had serious environmental impacts.

Figure 2.9 A sailed Polynesian catamaran.

Activity 2.4   Island colonisation as an ancient environmental challenge

What do you think would be the likely impacts of a Polynesian colonisation on the ecosystems of previously uninhabited Pacific islands? You will find it useful to refer back to the question about the anthropogenic causes of species extinction in Section 2.7. Write down a few points. Try to expand on your answers to explain why these impacts would be likely to occur – keeping in mind the characteristics of both the new arrivals and the previously established biological community.

Comment

Overexploitation As in Mauritius, birds and other island wildlife would have lacked defences and would have displayed naive behaviour when first encountering humans. This behaviour would have encouraged unsustainable exploitation. Overharvesting of useful trees or plants might also have been a risk.

Destruction of habitats The use of fire and other forms of clearance for cultivation, as well as felling trees for housing and building boats and canoes, could have had major impacts on the composition of ecosystems and habitats.

Bioinvasion Pigs, dogs and rats would all have had serious impacts. As you have seen, island fauna – especially flightless and ground-nesting birds – are usually unaccustomed to predatory and scavenging mammals. Some introduced plants might also be expected to proliferate.

You might have noted that, although settlers and their accompanying species may be arriving from islands that are no great distance apart, the levels of evolutionary specialisation on islands tend to ensure a high degree of differentiation between their species. This means that much of the previous experience of ecosystem exploitation of newly arriving human groups would not be directly transferable to their new home. Also keep in mind that some voyages of settlement, such as the colonisation of Aotearoa (the Maori name for New Zealand), involved long journeys to very unfamiliar environments. Although the colonisation of Aotearoa was clearly successful, there is evidence of numerous bird extinctions. Smaller islands could be even more vulnerable. In the far east of the Pacific Ocean, the island of Rapa Nui (the local name for Easter Island) is one of the most notorious cases of ecosystem collapse.

Archaeologists now believe that the collapse of Rapa Nui came about primarily through the overexploitation of forests, as a result of the demands arising from the construction and transportation of the monumental stone sculptures the island is now famous for (Figure 2.10). After the loss of vegetative cover and soil erosion came social conflict and population collapse – with a decrease from an estimated 10 000 people in the 17th century to a few thousand a century later (Bahn and Flenley, 1992). Drought and introduced Polynesian rats may have also played a part, but so too did the end of contact with other islands inhabited by Polynesian people. The loss of timber spelled the end of the construction of large, ocean-going boats (Figure 2.9), which precluded the sharing of resources and ideas with other islanders – or any relocation by the people of Rapa Nui.

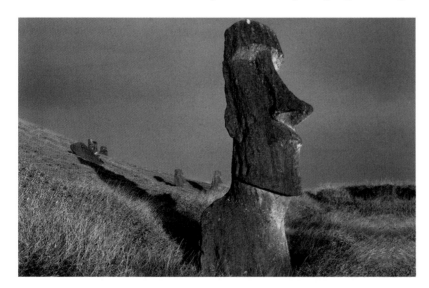

Figure 2.10   Monolithic sculptures (*moai*) on the island of Rapa Nui (Easter Island).

However, although it is salutary, Rapa Nui is an extreme case. Across most of the Pacific the long-term success of Polynesian occupation suggests an eventual coming to terms with the ecological opportunities and challenges of new islands.

2.9   Coevolution of ecosystems and social systems

It is not only human beings who adapt to new conditions. Existing biological communities and incoming species must adjust to each other if both are to survive. Through the process of **coevolution** the different parts of an ecosystem come to fit together through mutual changes that take place over time. Coevolution is not fundamentally different when one of the species in question is *Homo sapiens*, although the challenge can be tough when humans arrive suddenly. You have already encountered several situations in which human actions have prompted ecosystems to fall apart or degrade.

In Chapter 1 you saw that the term now used for such misguided interventions is that they are 'unsustainable'. Successful coevolution is thus vital to sustainability. As a generalisation, human–ecosystem interaction is more sustainable when coevolution between social systems and ecosystems is strong, and less sustainable when coevolution is weak. Not surprisingly, then, Europeans bringing ideas, habits and living things from a distant land mass to a tropical island pose a greater challenge to coevolution and sustainability than islanders on shorter migrations. However, both are at risk of triggering serious changes in the new ecosystems they encounter.

Without a penchant for migration, the human species might well have stayed put in its earliest homeland – the rift valleys of East Africa – and never ventured to all the other regions of the planet. This mobility escalated when the Austronesian people pioneered 'blue water' sailing, and it further accelerated some five or six centuries ago with a surge of European oceanic voyaging. These and other human journeys and migrations were the predecessors of the more encompassing and intensive globalisation of the contemporary world.

This chapter has looked at some of these early steps on the way to globalisation because they can teach us some important lessons. Today, environmental problems such as climate change or pollution often overflow the borders of individual countries. This is a significant point, and it has contributed to the way people now think about the world as a single, interconnected place. But it is also vital to remember that environmental problems do not just emerge out of modern, developed countries and flow outwards. The accounts of early long-distance migrations show us that environmental disturbance is closely associated with the movement of people beyond the places or regions they were familiar with. This reminds us that environmental problems go back a very long time – well before modern nation states or forms of production existed.

Clearly, human mobility should not be seen in just a negative way –without migrations and journeys, humans would not have populated most of the planet, and much of the biodiversity of each inhabited part of the world would not exist. But it is important to keep in mind that, wherever there is long-distance movement, there is likely to be an attenuation or a break in the coevolution of social systems and ecosystems. There will be high levels of uncertainty in the dealings with the new environment that come from ignorance or lack of experience, which greatly heightens the risk of unsustainable behaviour. Often, however, people who have migrated long distances do not become aware of the shortfall in their knowledge until disasters occur.

You have seen that the word 'governance' comes from an old nautical term. It is also interesting to note that the word 'disaster' – which is used so often today in relation to environmental mishaps – also has a root in navigation. It means, literally, to lose your star – from the Greek *astron*, meaning star. When you sail far enough for the stars to look different, it is time to be very careful!

How humans adapt to new environments in the long term has a biological dimension, like any form of adaptation. But it also has a very strong cultural and social dimension because it involves learning and social organisation. How a group governs itself, or steers its development, plays a major part. Governance is not simply about managing people and their social relationships. It is also about managing and directing our relationships with the physical world and the ecosystems that we are part of. How societies govern themselves evolves over time, just as all living organisms adapt and evolve. As you saw in the case of European island colonies, governance with a strong element of learning 'from the bottom' has a better chance of nurturing sustainable practices than governance coming 'from the top' – especially when that 'top' is some place far away.

Where ordinary people are working with, and observing changes in, the environment, they usually have a much better chance of feeding useful ideas and suggestions into the steering of their societies than smaller elite groups whose dealings with the environment are more remote. Governance, in this sense, is a vital part of the coevolutionary processes that lead in the direction of sustainability.

This chapter has shown that the particular conditions of island environments account for both the special creativity and the extreme vulnerability of island life. You have also seen that lessons from islands can be useful for the mainland; islands having worked as a kind of early warning system for environmental problems later faced by the rest of the world. In Chapter 3 you find out more about physical systems that are variable and turbulent – and how societies cope with them. This takes you away from islands and on to larger land masses. It picks up on the issue of how societies steer or manage themselves in the face of variability in their environments and looks more closely at the question of governance in a global context.

2.10   Summary of Chapter 2

2.1   The discovery of uninhabited oceanic islands played an important strategic role in the era of European maritime expansion around the globe.

2.2   The natural endowments and felicitous location of oceanic islands prompted comparisons with the biblical 'Garden of Eden' in the imagination of European settlers.

2.3   The disastrous impact of provisioning stopovers and settlement on small oceanic islands gave European colonists an early experience of environmental degradation. It was a forerunner of what is now called 'unsustainable development'.

2.4   Oceanic islands provided important early lessons about the vulnerability of island wildlife to human impacts, including invasion by introduced animals.

Once you have completed the Questions for Chapter 2, you should go to the course website and finish any activities you have not yet completed.

2.5   Settlers and administrators on small island colonies learned some important lessons about the governance of their societies – and especially about managing their relationship with the environment – from their experience of environmental degradation.

2.6   The main legacy of the early European experience of uninhabited oceanic islands has been the idea that the ideal landscape is a 'pristine' one, devoid of any noticeable human alteration.

2.7   The privileging of unspoilt wilderness as the ideal model of nature in the western imagination has had a major impact on the imagery of both the tourist industry and modern environmentalism.

2.8   Studies of island species gave pioneering evolutionary theorists such as Darwin and Wallace important insights into the processes of diversification of living organisms.

2.9   The same processes that contribute to the peculiar creativity of island environments with regard to biological diversification also make island species especially vulnerable to environmental changes. This has been manifested in high rates of extinction of island fauna.

2.10   Polynesian colonisation of oceanic islands seems to have had deleterious effects on island ecosystems in much the same way as European settlement led to severe environmental disturbance on islands.

2.11   The lack of coevolution between human social systems and ecosystems – particularly after human migration – is a significant contributing factor to unsustainable practices.

Questions for Chapter 2

Question 2.1

Which of the following statements, if any, are characteristics of ecosystems?

(a) They include interacting organisms and their physical environment.

(b) Each organism belongs to one ecosystem only.

(c) The degree of interconnectivity between its parts gives an ecosystem its distinctiveness.

(d) Ecosystems are open to flows of energy but closed to flows of matter.

(e) Ecosystems and social systems should be treated separately.

Question 2.2

List four useful services that an oceanic island might have offered a 17th-century crew stopping over on a long sea voyage.

Question 2.3

Describe, in a maximum of 70 words, the environmental problems that followed the deforestation of small islands as identified by early European colonists.

Question 2.4

List four characteristics of the dodo that made it particularly vulnerable to the predatory animals introduced to Mauritius.

Question 2.5

Explain, in two or three sentences, how the notion of 'governance' differs from that of 'government'.

Question 2.6

Put the following statements in the correct historical order.

(a) The idea of wilderness is established as a mainstay of modern environmentalism and tourism.

(b) European seafarers discover uninhabited islands far out in the ocean.

(c) Uncultivated lands become rare around the European seaboard.

(d) As the development of North America and other 'new worlds' proceeds, people become increasingly nostalgic for uncultivated, undisturbed 'wilderness'.

(e) The idea of undefiled 'Edens' is transferred from uninhabited islands to other newly discovered regions that are already populated.

(f) The idea of islands as pristine, undefiled 'Edens' cements itself in the European imagination.

Question 2.7

Which of the following, if any, are characteristics of island ecosystems?

(a) Island species are often clearly related to nearby mainland species.

(b) The organisms that find their way to islands are genetically suited to island life.

(c) Island species may diverge from their mainland relatives in pronounced and unusual ways.

(d) On a cluster of islands, the descendants of a single population of organisms often differ from island to island.

(e) How a species evolves on an island is determined by the random cluster of genes carried by its founder population.

Question 2.8

Explain, in two or three sentences, how human disturbance and natural variability can work together as causes of extinction of island species.

Question 2.9

Assess the following statement, in no more than 130 words.

The species introduced by Polynesian explorers slotted comfortably into the ecosystems of newly discovered Pacific islands because they were brought from other Pacific islands.

Question 2.10

Which of the following statements, if any, are correct interpretations of the concept of coevolution?

(a) Humans have only coevolved with the East African ecosystems in which they originated.

(b) Humans coevolve quickly wherever they go because of their culture and social organisation.

(c) Long-distance migration generally makes coevolution between humans and their new ecosystems more difficult to accomplish than shorter moves.

(d) Learning from common, everyday experience can assist societies in the process of coevolution with unfamiliar ecosystems.

References

Bahn, P. and Flenley, J. (1992) *Easter Island, Earth Island*, London, Thames and Hudson.

Darwin, C. (1996) *The Origin of Species*, 6th edn (first published 1859), Oxford, Oxford University Press.

Dening, G. (1992) *Mr Bligh's Bad Language: Passion, Power and Theatre on the Bounty*, Cambridge and New York, Cambridge University Press.

Fischer, S. (2002) *A History of the Pacific Islands* (Chapter 1), New York, Palgrave.

Grove, R.H. (1995) *Green Imperialism: Colonial Expansion, Tropical Island Edens and the Origins of Environmentalism 1600–1860*, Cambridge, Cambridge University Press.

MacArthur, R.H. and Wilson, E.O. (1963) *The Theory of Island Biogeography*, Princeton, NJ, Princeton University Press.

Pyne, S.J. (1997) *Vestal Fire*, Seattle and London, University of Washington Press.

Quammen, D. (1996) *The Song of the Dodo: Island Biogeography in an Age of Extinctions*, London, Pimlico.

Rampino, M. and Caldeira, K. (1994) 'The Goldilocks problem: climatic evolution and long-term habitability of terrestrial planets', *Annual Review of Astronomy and Astrophysics*, vol. 32, pp. 83–114.

World Resources Institute (WRI) (2000) *World Resources 2000–2001 People and Ecosystems: The Fraying Web of Life*, Washington, DC, World Resources Institute.

Chapter 3
Weathering the extremes: the challenge of dynamic systems

3.1   Introduction

The human contribution to climate change is difficult to pin down, as you have seen, because of the natural fluctuations of geoclimatic systems. All life has to weather these ups and downs, along with occasional upheavals such as fire, disease or geological activity. One implication of this is that the human impact on biological communities rarely operates alone. As you learned from looking at island life, human-induced stress can push a species or community into the danger zone – but the final blow may be delivered by nothing more than the 'ordinary' extremes of environmental variability.

However, it would be a mistake to let our concern with the vulnerability of living things overwhelm our appreciation of life's achievements. In the face of all the challenges posed by variable conditions and extreme events, life flourishes over most of the planet. As you saw in Chapter 2, ecosystems endure and thrive because they can adjust and adapt. And this endurance, of course, also applies to human life, which has prevailed through times of great variability and upheaval.

This chapter engages more closely with the dynamics of physical and living systems, and what they mean for human social life. Some of the changes that living systems go through are extremely hard to predict, and this uncertainty can present enormous challenges to the human groups who depend on them. The chapter starts with marine ecosystems, which are vital to many island communities, and moves on to the interplay of climate systems and agricultural systems, which operate on much larger scales and shape the lives of millions of people.

How we live with the uncertainty that is inherent in the physical world is not just a problem of understanding nature but also a question of organising ourselves. How can we best steer our societies through rough patches? How should we govern ourselves and our activities so as not to be caught off guard by extremes or sudden shifts in the physical systems we depend on?

These issues are present at every level of human social existence – from the local right up to the global. After reviewing some earlier 'experiments' in governing social systems on a major scale, this chapter opens up the question of global governance, in the context of the many forms of connectivity that now appear to bind humans together across great distances.

3.2   Reef wars: catastrophe and the coral–seaweed competition

As you have seen, island ecosystems are particularly sensitive to environmental change. While Chapter 2 concentrated on land-based birds, terrestrial species are not necessarily the top priority of the people who live on islands and atolls.

Figure 3.1   Coral, sponge and sea rod. Field of view is approximately 1 m across.

Marine life is often closest to the heart of small island communities and at the core of the marine ecosystem, in tropical oceans, are coral reefs. In terms of their biodiversity, coral reef ecosystems have often been compared to tropical rainforests.

Coral creates its own substrate, as the skeletons of the coral polyps gradually build up over the years into structures of considerable size (Figure 3.1). Not only are entire islands composed of coral (Figure 3.2) but also encircling reefs protect islands from the eroding effects of wind and wave. Without this 'barrier' effect, it would be difficult or impossible for many islands to build up functioning terrestrial ecosystems.

Figure 3.2   The coral island of Ambergris Caye, Belize, Central America.

For very many generations, island and coastal people have harvested the rich marine life on and around coral reefs. More recently, coral reefs have emerged as a major attraction for tourists, as the Maldivian people know well. But the popular appreciation of the coral ecosystem has a dark side. Since the 1980s, evidence from the Pacific and Indian Oceans and the Caribbean has been building into a real fear over the future of coral reefs and the people who depend on them. As the articles on the Maldives in Chapter 1 suggest, this concern is linked with global climate change.

The problem stems from the fact that coral can only live in water within a narrow temperature range of approximately 25–29 °C. When this temperature is exceeded, there is a disturbance in the relationship between corals and the microscopic algae called **zooxanthellae** living within them. Zooxanthellae give coral reefs the rich coloration they are renowned for but, more importantly, they provide nutrients through photosynthesis.

Rising temperature stresses the corals, which expel their zooxanthellae, turning white or 'bleaching' as a result. Bleached coral may recover after a short period of slight warming, but a temperature rise for more than six months is likely to prove fatal. Whole reefs are now said to be endangered, with implications for all levels of the tropical marine ecosystem.

In this way, the degradation of coral reefs has emerged as one of the key symptoms of global warming, adding new weight to the idea that islands are the planet's environmental early warning systems.

However, there is more to the problem than this. The dynamics of the coral reef ecosystem are not a simple case of growing human impact leading to mounting coral mortality. Instead, there are surprises in store, and the nature of these 'surprises' has some rather important lessons for our understanding of ecosystem dynamics.

For a start, there are more variables affecting coral than just temperature. One of the main factors is the part played by the main competitor of coral – fleshy macro-algae – otherwise known as seaweed. When corals are weak and distressed, macro-algae have a tendency to move in, smothering the reefs and establishing their own 'regime'.

In this play-off between two potentially dominant forms of reef life, several variables can tip the balance. Storm damage can affect coral; so too can a decrease in the population of the fish species that graze on seaweed and keep it in check. An increase in the nutrient loading of the water can cause the zooxanthellae to grow too large or too fast, harming the coral.

Each of these factors occurs naturally, and each can work in combination with temperature-induced bleaching. As you might have noticed, each of them can also have a human component.

Figure 3.3   Coral reefs are a major tourist attraction.

■   Along with anthropogenic global warming, what other human impacts do you think might contribute to the advance of macro-algae at the expense of coral?

☐   Anthropogenic climate change could be increasing storm frequency and severity. Sewage and agricultural runoff contribute to nutrient loading. Overfishing removes a check on macro-algae.

Human damage to coral reefs can also be more direct, as in the case of destruction for coastal development, anchor damage and souvenir taking. Add this to the overfishing and sewage problem, and you are back with the trade-off between development and sustainability described in Chapter 1. Clearly, global-scale climate change is not the only issue. The pressure of human numbers on a tropical island can also jeopardise the very attractions that bring visitors: a big dilemma for islands dependent on tourist revenue (Figure 3.3).

In this light, you might expect islanders to keep a very close watch on the war between coral and macro-algae, and to use this information as an indicator of stress on the ecosystem. However, it is not quite that simple. It turns out that the amount of coral and macro-algae present may not be a particularly useful sign of the health of the coral reef ecosystem.

It comes down to the dynamics of the reef ecosystem. The coral regime and the macro-algal regime are **alternative stable states** of the reef ecosystem. At any moment, either 'regime' is likely to be dominant, but the system is much less likely to be found in any intermediate state where coral and macro-algae are both present. Once a certain threshold of stress has been crossed, the switch between coral and macro-algae tends to be quite sudden (Scheffer et al., 2001).

Does this situation sound familiar? In Chapter 1, you encountered a climatic system with the potential of rapidly switching between two 'states' or 'phases'.

■   Which massive landform is at risk of such a shift, and what term is given to this sort of event?

☐   The landform is the West Antarctic Ice Sheet and the process is known as a 'catastrophic shift' in a system.

As Chapter 1 suggests, many natural systems are vulnerable to catastrophic shifts between stable states. Although no state is more 'natural' than its alternative, the level of biodiversity supported by one state often far outweighs the other, making it vastly preferable to humans. Just as coral reefs are biologically richer than seaweed-smothered reefs (Figure 3.4), so too are clear lakes richer than lakes clouded with phytoplankton, and vegetated lands more life-supporting than parched deserts.

Figure 3.4   A coral reef being smothered by macro-algae.

An example of a change in state that seriously affects many people around the North Atlantic Ocean is the collapse of the cod population (Box 3.1). This example illustrates well the way in which events referred to as 'catastrophic' in scientific terms can also be experienced as 'catastrophes' in the everyday sense of the word. However, do not assume that *all* catastrophic events are detrimental to humans.

Box 3.1 Alternative stable states: the fate of cod

The coastal waters of the North Atlantic, around Newfoundland, Canada, were once alive with Atlantic cod (*Gadus morhua*), which occurred in legendary abundance. Huge quantities of fish were taken from these grounds in the 19th and 20th centuries. When fears were expressed that the stocks might become exhausted, the highly influential zoologist Thomas Henry Huxley (1825–1895) responded that 'Any tendency to overfishing will meet with its natural check in the diminution of supply'. These words, delivered to an international gathering on fisheries in 1883, gave scientific credence to the notion that overfishing could not occur and that the seas offer a limitless bounty of food (Kurlansky, 1999). This view is still common today, although there is now plenty of evidence to the contrary.

When cod stocks in Newfoundland waters crashed in the 1980s, they were expected to recover, as they had done a century earlier after another decline. The Canadian government introduced a moratorium on cod fishing in the 1990s, and scientists and fishers began to wait for stocks to recover. It now appears that they may wait in vain. Other overfished stock, such as herring (*Clupea harengus*) in the North Sea, appear to be able to recover when fishing is reduced. Could cod be different? There is no certain answer to this question but there is a plausible theory that the marine ecosystem supporting cod fisheries has two alternative stable states: one with cod in tremendous abundance and one with very low numbers. If this is true, the cod population may never recover.

The key to this theory lies in the ecology of cod. It is a large, predatory fish which feeds on smaller predatory species of fish. The prey of the smaller predatory species includes the fry of the cod. As long as large cod are present in abundance, populations of the smaller predators are held in check by predation, which permits sufficient cod fry to escape to maintain a healthy population of cod. However, when adult cod numbers are drastically reduced, fewer small predators are eaten and their population rises. A higher population of small predatory fish means that fewer cod fry escape predation and so the population of adult cod cannot increase. Cod are locked into permanently low abundance (Pauly et al., 2002).

Our growing knowledge of the susceptibility of many ecosystems to catastrophic shifts has enormous implications for the way we engage with environmental issues. Along with much of western science, the study of environmental problems has tended to seek out simple cause-and-effect relationships. We are still more used to thinking in terms of changing conditions that give rise to corresponding changes in natural systems in a gradual, or an incremental way (recall the ball bearing rolling along a flat surface in Box 1.2).

If we assume that change is incremental, we can also assume that there is an opportunity to step back and reassess what we are doing if our impacts on a natural system seem too severe. But the potential for catastrophic shifts challenges this assumption, because of the suddenness of the shift between states (the ball bearing dropping off the table). Once the shift becomes apparent, it is generally too late to stop it. And once it is over, it can be extremely difficult to reverse it and return to the old state or regime. In the case of coral reefs, for example, the heavy presence of macro-algae prevents the resettlement of coral larvae, even when these larvae are plentiful.

3.2.1   Tangling with complex systems

How can an ecosystem transform so suddenly even when the conditions that promote such a shift may be changing only gradually?

There is no easy answer, but the capacity for this sort of transformation has much to do with the complexity of living systems. What defines an ecosystem, as you saw in Chapter 2, is the degree of interconnectivity between its parts. Ecosystems and other biological systems (including social systems) belong to the category of **complex systems**, which means that they have not only many components but also many connections between these components and with the world beyond the system itself.

The richness of these connections gives complex systems properties not found in less 'well-connected' systems. Most importantly, complex systems are dynamic or adaptive: they can change over time in response to changing conditions. What makes this possible are the loops in the internal connections of the system, which means that the effects of an activity can pass through a chain of connections and feed back into the system.

Through many 'iterations' or cycles of **feedback**, a complex system can reorganise its parts and their connections, developing new pathways or ways of doing things. Less complex systems may have many parts, but they lack the loops of interconnectivity that enable such adjustments.

In the case of biological systems, this capacity for adjustment is clearly a rather momentous quality, for it allows living things to both maintain their integrity in the face of changing conditions and, under certain circumstances, to transform themselves.

Feedback loops can dampen down the effects of change to help a system stay stable, just like the helmsman in Chapter 2, who keeps the ship on course. This is termed **negative feedback**. It happens when living coral adjusts to small changes in ocean temperature and succeeds in keeping its internal state within the limits needed for survival.

Feedback can also amplify the effects of change, as in cases where the system's response to change promotes further change. This sort of self-reinforcing cycle of effects is termed **positive feedback**. For example, this is what happens when a population grows rapidly, with new members of the population adding to the potential for further growth. Positive feedback opens up the possibility of major transformations in the state of a system.

In the case of coral ecosystems, both forms of feedback are occurring. Up to a point, negative feedback keeps the coral regime stable, but once stress pushes the coral past its tolerance levels, change-inducing positive feedback rapidly takes over: macro-algae proliferate and the coral dies.

From the human point of view, the real challenge is working out the current state of a system: where it's at, and what it's likely to do next.

■ Recalling Chapter 1, why is it difficult to predict if or when a catastrophic shift in a system is imminent?

☐ Systems typically lack recognisable warning signals that a change is coming.

Warning signs may be present, but the trouble is that they tend to be beyond our comprehension. To the observer, the ecosystem looks stable and healthy, despite the fact that it may be approaching a threshold.

So, if the observable state of a complex living system does not give enough clues about its current state, is there any other way of finding out?

Today, computers offer a window into the dynamics of complex systems. They do this by enabling us to construct and run a 'model' of the system. This process entails writing down a mathematical relationship (equation) for each of the links within the ecosystem. These equations will show how one part of an ecosystem is expected to change if another component is altered.

However, as you will see, even computer modelling cannot make complex systems fully transparent and predictable.

3.2.2   Computer modelling of complex systems

A computer model attempts to simplify a very complex natural system. As you may have noted, this process inevitably reduces some of the complexity that makes a complex system what it is, but it is currently the best option.

■ Which prediction made by a computer model do most people encounter on a daily basis?

☐ Weather forecasts are made with computer models.

This example suggests that we *can* re-create a complex system with a computer, although anyone with experience of weather forecasting will tell you that these models are not always accurate! So why *are* computer models sometimes not correct?

Recall the characteristics of a complex system: its richness of internal and external links. To model the coral reef ecosystem correctly we must understand, for example, how much coral will die if, say, one 'unit' of macro-algae was added. To determine this effect we need to do the experiment. This could mean a laboratory or a field experiment with live coral and macro-algae, which would entail killing the coral with the macro-algae gradually and watching the results very carefully. We could then draw a graph of the effect of the macro-algae concentration on the viability of the coral, which might resemble Figure 3.5.

You can see in Figure 3.5 at the start of adding the macro-algae to the system, not very much coral dies at first. Then, all of a sudden, the coral dies very rapidly.

Now that we have a graph, we can write down an equation that will say what we think will happen if any amount of algae is added. An equation to describe what

Figure 3.5 Schematic graph of the mortality of coral when macro-algae are added to the system.

is happening in Figure 3.5 is fairly straightforward. However, the difficulty is that we have an equation for just one component of a complex system.

■ Which three other components of the coral ecosystem may change the shape of the graph in Figure 3.5?

☐ Temperature, nutrient loading and a decline in the grazers of macro-algae (i.e. fish).

Each of these three components will affect the shape of the graph, but we don't know how much they will affect it. This is difficult to work out because of the many different ways in which these components can interact. There is not just one form of feedback but multiple, entangled feedbacks. The multiplicity of feedbacks can turn a simple graph with a predictable relationship between coral and macro-algae numbers into a graph with an unpredictable catastrophic shift.

So, although we can experiment on one component of a system to see what happens, it is much harder to experiment on a system with multiple feedbacks – which are very difficult to separate and untangle. In other words, what makes a complex system dynamic and flexible also makes it hard to understand.

By using a computer we can vary the equations that link the components and feedbacks to gain a better understanding of how the system will change, including how the feedbacks will change. For the weather you can get a very good forecast of what will happen tomorrow. But you probably would not trust a weather forecast for a day two months in the future. If we understood *all* of the components and *all* of the feedback loops, it should be possible (for a brilliant mathematician) to predict the weather or the state of a coral reef ecosystem at any time in the future. However, in the real world, there will always be some components and feedbacks that are missed or inadequately accounted for – and they can make all the difference. So, while the current models are very good for some situations, they are not so good for pinpointing the moment when catastrophic shifts will occur in complex systems.

For all its limitations, however, computer modelling has had a tremendous effect on our society and the way we view the future, as you will see in Book 3.

3.3   Sustainability and ecosystem dynamics

The daunting challenge of anticipating what complex dynamic systems will do next means that wherever there is complexity in the world – from the human point of view – there is also uncertainty. And all living systems are complex. So what does this mean for human communities whose livelihoods rely on their local ecosystems? What does it mean, more generally, for our current quest for sustainability?

Arguably, the early discussions of sustainability did not give enough attention to the variability of natural systems. But more recent work suggests growing sensitivity towards the dynamic qualities of the natural world, as evidenced by the way the World Resources Institute (WRI) frames the issue of sustainability. In its words:

> The challenge for the 21st century is to understand the vulnerabilities and resilience of ecosystems so that we can find ways to reconcile the demands of human development with the tolerances of nature.
>
> (WRI, 2000, p. 40)

Resilience means the capacity of a system to maintain its state in the face of stress or shock. **Vulnerability** is the other side of resilience, meaning the likelihood that stress or disturbance will fundamentally alter the system.

You should now have a sense of the immensity of the challenge that the WRI is setting out. As you have seen, the difficulty of predicting when systems will change implies that vulnerability and resilience are not readily observable qualities. They are properties of a system that emerge out of many tangled and iterated loops of effects, in ways that no simple 'snapshot' of the system can reveal.

These loops or feedbacks stretch through time – sometimes quite significant amounts of time. This can make it very difficult to link human activities to the undermining of natural resilience.

■ From what you read about island ecosystems in Chapter 2, why may there be time lags between human interventions and their repercussions on ecosystems?

☐ The lowering of the ecosystems' resilience may only become apparent during extremes of environmental variability.

In the case of coral reefs, nutrient loading or overfishing may have reduced the resilience of the ecosystem, but this might not be revealed until a hurricane (Figure 3.6) or a heatwave provides the final blow.

Figure 3.6   Hurricane waves striking the coast of an island.

The study of ecosystem dynamics suggests that the best way to look after the ecosystems we value is not to try preventing all disturbance, but to minimise the human impacts that undermine resilience.

The main source of resilience in an ecosystem is **redundancy** – the back-ups, 'spare parts' or alternative pathways that are available in the system. In simple systems (for example, most human-built machines), each component is committed to a specific task. But in living systems and other complex dynamic systems, as you have seen, there is a certain flexibility that allows for adaptability or adjustment. What makes this possible is redundancy.

A high level of redundancy gives a system a kind of uncommitted potentiality for change – so it can absorb stress or shocks without major changes of state. In ecosystems, this usually takes the form of duplication and diversification of function – such as the presence of species with overlapping ecological roles or niches.

■ With this in mind, why do you think island ecosystems have been especially vulnerable to human impact?

☐ The challenge of colonising islands and surviving in restricted areas tends to result in a high degree of specialisation. This is another way of saying that island ecosystems tend to have a relatively low level of redundancy.

3.3.1   Learning how to harvest ecosystems

As you saw in Chapter 2, when human groups colonise a new territory they often view its biological communities as 'bounty' for unrestrained harvest. Until there is experience of the level of exploitation that an ecosystem can tolerate, destructive impacts are likely to continue. But colonists need also to sample the variability and fluctuation in the ecosystems they depend on because the maximum sustainable harvest or yield in a 'good' season may be very different from that in a 'bad' season.

Generally, the longer a social group inhabits a region, the greater the range of variability they will have experienced – including the variability their own activities have induced or amplified. This suggests that those human groups who have successfully occupied an area for very many generations – people who are often termed 'indigenous' – have learned to weather the extremes as well as the moderate phases of 'their' physical and ecological systems.

This learning process can be seen as a kind of feedback, with human beings in the loop. In cases where change is gradual or steady, this feedback is like that of the helmsman who plays the role of the 'governor' in the system, responding in an ongoing way to changes that can be seen or felt. But in most cases, as you have seen, the complexity of ecosystems means that human activity is caught up in a multitude of mutually entangled feedback loops, which makes for much more indirect and uncertain relationships between human communities and ecosystems.

For most of the span of human evolution this uncertainty was negotiated by leaving ecosystems largely intact. As **hunters and gatherers** (Figure 3.7), the human role in ecosystems was (and, in some cases, still is) one of 'tweaking' or tuning rather than controlling. The fraction of total biological production of the system that was consumed was low: probably somewhere around 0.1% (Marten, 2001, Chapter 3). Today, there are still parts of the world where communities, using knowledge accrued over many generations, collectively manage their 'harvesting' of natural ecosystems in a way that does not undermine their resilience. A good example is the way some island communities 'govern' their use of coral reefs.

Figure 3.7   Coral reef fishing in the Red Sea, Sudan.

However, new questions of management arise once **agricultural production** takes root. With the development of agriculture, a much higher percentage of biological production is made available for human consumption.

Evidence suggests that the domestication of plants and animals may have begun as a response to a reduction in the resources available from natural ecosystems, caused by a period of drier conditions in the Middle East some 12 000 years ago.

Restructuring an ecosystem so that a relatively high proportion of biological production is channelled to human consumers entails a radical simplification of the living system. Humans attempt to cut out those species that compete with them for nutrients ('weeds' or 'vermin'). This results in many components and pathways found in the natural ecosystem no longer being present in the **agroecosystem**. After that, numerous functions once performed naturally by ecosystems, such as seed sowing, watering and soil fertilising, have to be done by humans (Figure 3.8a, b).

Figure 3.8 (a) Terraced slopes in Peru. Terracing hillsides is a long-established agricultural technique that traps and conserves both water and nutrients. (b) Harvesting rice in Guilin, China.

Successive improvements in agricultural technology, such as better water supply or pest control or higher crop yields, all increase the flow of nutrients to the human part of the system. If this is successful, progressively larger human populations can be supported by a fixed area of land. Historically, this was the main attraction of agricultural development.

■ From what you have learned about ecosystem dynamics, what do you think would be the main drawback of a simplified agroecosystem?

☐ An agroecosystem is much less resilient to shocks or stresses than a natural ecosystem because redundancy is lost.

The more tightly controlled the agroecosystem is, the less humans can rely on the natural working of the system to absorb the effects of climatic extremes (such as drought or heavy rainfall) or upheavals (such as outbreaks of pests or disease).

This means that agricultural societies, if they are to survive environmental variability, have to build replacements into the system for the natural redundancy that has been lost. Historically, this took many forms, including storing water and stockpiling crop surpluses from good years. It also involved increasing contact with other societies to gain access to their resources – either through trade or through the more aggressive strategies of plunder and conquest. To put it in contemporary terms, these are the ways in which agricultural societies confront the challenge of sustainability.

The feedback between a hunter–gatherer community and its ecosystem was mentioned earlier. Picking up on signs about the state of the ecosystem and collectively processing and responding to these indicators is a form of governance: a way in which human communities steer and manage themselves, and their relationships with their environment. In an agricultural society, the ecosystem humans rely on may have been made *less* complex but this, in turn, can make the problem of governing the social system rather *more* involved.

This has much to do with the extra work that is required to take over functions once performed by natural ecosystems – including the need to cope with fluctuations and shocks once absorbed by these more complex systems. Organising labour to maintain the agroecosystem, dealing with surpluses and shortfalls, and managing the exchanges with neighbouring societies all create new challenges for governing a society.

Today, the question is how to steer our societies through the environmental changes that are now happening on a global scale. This is clearly an immense challenge. However, if we keep in mind that large and complex societies have faced the problem of organising themselves through environmental extremes and shocks many times in the past, there may be lessons we can learn.

The next section completes this journey away from small islands by heading to the great river valleys of India and China. For thousands of years, the agricultural production of these regions has supported some of the largest and highest density human populations on the planet – but not without some major setbacks.

3.4   Heavy weather: agriculture and climatic variability

The long and gradual development of agroecosystems and the rise of rural populations in India and China share much with traditional or 'peasant' agricultural societies the world over. A common theme in these societies is the alternation between periods of relative comfort – often nostalgically termed 'Golden Ages' – and times of great hardship. Hard times can arise out of war and other social unrest, but most often the leading role has been played by environmental adversity.

In South and East Asia, the most important environmental variable is the climatic pattern known as the **monsoon**. In contrast to the temperate regions, with their more evenly spread rainfall, monsoonal regions (Figure 3.9) have an extreme seasonal variation in rainfall, the summer rains providing the vast majority of the year's precipitation (75–90% of annual rainfall in India, for example). A so-called good monsoon season is usually one with above-average rainfall (Figure 3.10a), while a poor season has a rainfall deficit. Above all, 'drought' (Figure 3.10b) – the delay, interruption or absence of the crucial summer rains – is the major environmental threat for monsoonal Asia.

Figure 3.9   Regions affected by monsoon climates in the Eastern Hemisphere.

Figure 3.10   (a) Monsoon rainfall. (b) The impact of drought on the soil surface.

It is now well understood that behind the refrain of 'golden' and 'gloomy' years are patterns of climatic fluctuation, with long-term records showing distinct phases of above and below average monsoonal rainfall. However, research suggests that the rhythms of monsoonal variation do not work alone. Since the 1970s climate scientists have begun to decipher the workings of another cycle of climatic variability with even wider influence than the fluctuations of the monsoon. This phenomenon is known as the **El Niño Southern Oscillation**, and its effects on global climate are staggering (Box 3.2).

Box 3.2 The El Niño Southern Oscillation (ENSO)

El Niño means 'the Christ Child' or, more literally, 'the boy'. It comes from South America where very warm surface water appears on the western coast within a few months of Christmas. The phenomenon was known for centuries in South America but it was only in 1972 – the 'year of the climate anomalies' – that much of the rest of the world really took notice. A massive pool of warm water appeared off the South American coast and upset rainfall around the globe. There were devastating droughts in Africa, India, Australia and the former Soviet Union. At the same time, there was abnormally heavy rainfall in the Mediterranean and along the South American coast, causing extensive flooding.

The physical cause for this natural event is a change in the pattern of winds in the southwestern Pacific Ocean, which allows warm water effectively to slop into a different part of the ocean. Because the water cycle depends on evaporation from the ocean and evaporation depends on the temperature of the water, this warm water alters the amount of moisture the clouds can pick up. Clouds sometimes end up with much more moisture than usual, sometimes much less. When these clouds finally rain, people in Asia feel the effect of climate variation in the Pacific. These couplings of weather events in distant places are called **teleconnections**.

Generally, an ENSO happens every 2 to 8 years, although it is very difficult to untangle the cycles that drive it. When it does appear, the ENSO effect can vary greatly. The ENSO of 1972 was a major one.

Evidence suggests that the cycle of the Asian monsoon is not fundamentally controlled by the ENSO. But monsoons can be modified by it, and in a rather momentous way. When the monsoon cycle and the ENSO are phase-locked – i.e. when their respective peaks and troughs overlap – then adverse years can turn into very bad years indeed, with extremes of drought and flooding. It now appears that some of the worst famines in Asian history have occurred at times of monsoonal **phase-locking** with the ENSO.

In the years between 1870 and 1990 there were 11 occurrences of very strong ENSO episodes: in 1877, 1884, 1891, 1899, 1911, 1918, 1925, 1941, 1957, 1972 and 1982. In the case of India, the strong ENSOs of 1884, 1891, 1941 and 1957 did not result in severe deficits of rainfall. However, 1877, 1899, 1918 and 1972 were the worst years of drought recorded over this period (Figure 3.11). The evidence suggests it was only in these 4 years that the ENSO was phase-locked with a period of rainfall deficit in the Asian monsoon cycle (Kripalani and Kulkarni, 1997).

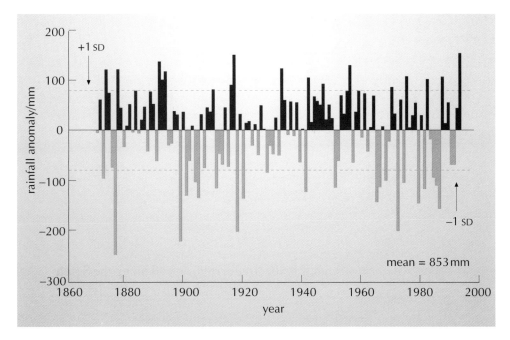

Figure 3.11   Graph of the deviations of rainfall in India. The dashed lines indicate ±1 standard deviation (SD) from the mean (853 mm).

Does this mean that the monsoonal lands of India and China are destined to disaster and poverty as a result of their unstable climates? Over the last 150 years, this argument has often been put forward by observers in wealthier, temperate countries, in order to explain the difference in living standards between 'tropical backwaters' and their own 'green and pleasant lands'.

Clearly, there is much more at stake. While the study of climate dynamics has advanced, researchers have not forgotten other factors that have also shaped the lives of people in the agricultural societies of India, China and elsewhere. We are now seeing some rather interesting attempts to combine new scientific understandings of weather and its effects with the kind of insights into the organisation of social life that social science can provide.

One of the questions of growing interest to researchers is how different societies have managed or steered themselves through good, bad and uncertain weather. As you saw above, this is a challenge that every agricultural society has faced.

By the 18th century, it has been argued, imperial China had a system of famine prevention and relief that operated from the state level downwards (Davis, 2001). In times of deficit, food held in provincial granaries was distributed to poor people in officially designated disaster areas, tax breaks were offered, and price controls were put in place to prevent speculation on foodstuffs. In better times, there was extensive state-organised work on infrastructure – such as improving irrigation and waterborne transportation.

Similar measures were taken in pre-colonial India. Although the centralised power of the imperial state did not match that of China, there are records of state level embargoes on food exports, widespread tax concessions and distribution of free food, as well as subsidies for well maintenance and irrigation work.

There was also a tradition of maintaining common lands, which were accessible to poor people.

These strategies might be seen as a kind of negative feedback in the agricultural social system: a form of response aimed at ameliorating the worst effects of environmental variability in order to maintain stability in the system. As a result of such measures, it has been claimed, widespread starvation was avoided even during a phase-locking of the ENSO and a monsoonal deficit in the mid-18th century (Davis, 2001).

Clearly, famine prevention and relief measures are preferable to no measures. However, there are also good reasons to be sceptical about the overall effectiveness of these strategies, as you will see.

3.4.1   Colonial catastrophes: the great famines

Just as the Asian monsoon and the ENSO came into phase in the mid-18th century, so too were there episodes of phase-locking in the late 19th century. As Figure 3.11 shows, these were centred on the years 1877 and 1899, and they seem to have been even more pronounced than the 18th-century episode. However, this may not be the most crucial difference.

By the late 19th century, much of India had been incorporated in the British Empire and was administered by British officials working in tandem with a powerful local elite (Figure 3.12). Although China was not politically annexed, European economic influence was strong there also. Recent research suggests the implications of this change for steering these societies through a phase of climatic extremes was profound.

Figure 3.12   Lord Lytton (1831–1891), the Viceroy of India during the famine of the 1870s.

Activity 3.1   The great famines: coping (or not coping) with crisis

(a) Recapping on what you read in this section, list five measures taken in pre-colonial India or late imperial China to prepare for and deal with drought.

(b) From the excerpt from *Late Victorian Holocausts*, make a comparative list of the ways in which British colonial administrators confronted drought.

Now read the three excerpts from *Late Victorian Holocausts* by social historian Mike Davis on the course website. Davis describes the response by the British administration to the famine in India and China in 1876–9. There is more detail than you require, but aim to get the gist of the argument.

As you will see, there are good reasons to be cautious about the effectiveness of pre-colonial measures for dealing with climatic uncertainty (Davis gives you some clues in the readings). Nevertheless, Davis's evidence suggests that the famines of the late 19th century were disasters without precedent. The human death toll of these two catastrophes in India and China is estimated at between 30 and 60 million people.

In many respects, Davis is presenting the gut-level experience of unsustainability in action. In keeping with what you have learned about catastrophic shifts, his account can be taken as a warning that the symptoms of unsustainability may not simply reveal themselves, step by step. Instead, they can erupt rapidly and disastrously.

(c) With this in mind, do you think the human and ecological disasters on the scale Davis describes might reappear? Write down your immediate impressions.

Comment

(a)

- Stabilisation of the prices of foodstuffs
- Relief operations using stockpiled grains and other food reserves
- Tax concessions
- State-subsidised maintenance of waterways, irrigation and flood control
- Common land accessible to poor people

(b)

- No food relief without forced labour
- Price of grain fixed by the 'free market'
- Surplus and available food committed to the export market
- No tax relief
- Privatisation and sale of common land

(c) There is no simple answer to this. But our growing knowledge of the possibility of major fluctuations in climate, and catastrophic shifts like the collapse of the West Antarctic Ice Sheet suggest we should take the question very seriously. You may want to revisit your responses to this question after reading the final sections of this chapter, and again at later points in the course.

So, what can we learn from the tragic famines of the late 19th century? What were their causes and how can we avoid their repetition?

Davis's message is that environmental variation alone cannot explain the magnitude of the 'great famines' of India and China. We must look to other variables too.

In the second half of the 19th century, Davis points out, India, China and many other agricultural economies were being incorporated into an emerging global economy. Instead of producing predominantly for local or regional needs, peasant farmers were encouraged, and often compelled (through taxation and other means), to produce for the global market. The result is that prices and conditions of work came to be set by distant market forces.

This led to some boom years in which agricultural production expanded and prices rose. But it also introduced a whole new kind of vulnerability into the social system.

As you have seen several times in this chapter, the greatest challenges to system stability occur when the extremes of different cycles coincide.

The strength of Davis's interpretation of the great famines is not only that he considers the effects of these physical systems but also that he takes account of another source of variability: the global economic system. Economic systems, like ecosystems, are complex and dynamic with their own rhythms. As anyone who has ever played the stock market or watched the movement of house prices will know, economies have ups and downs that are notoriously hard to predict. In the case of great 19th-century famines, Davis argues that climatic extremes coincided or phase-locked with a different kind of extreme: worldwide slumps in the global economy.

Newly enmeshed in this economy, and without the traditional reserves and relief to fall back on, peasant farmers across the colonial world were hit at once by economic depression and devastating drought. This meant that downward spirals in prices received for their produce coincided with drastic reductions in their crop harvests. In this way, the extreme effects in the climate system and the extreme events in the economy came together in a self-reinforcing loop: 'a fatal meshing of extreme events' with disastrous implications for the state of the agricultural system. The result was a 'catastrophe' in every sense of the word.

Now is a good time to do the website activities associated with this chapter.

3.4.2   The challenge of governing complex systems

It seems like a long journey from the problems of conserving coral reefs to the challenge of weathering extremes in agricultural societies. However, it should be apparent by now that some similar principles apply. In the dynamics of the coral reef ecosystem, the agricultural society and the global economy, there are multiple feedbacks, rendering it extremely difficult in each case to predict precisely any future state of the system.

■   In the face of such uncertainty, what is the best way of maintaining the resilience of the system?

☐   Ensuring there is redundancy or underused potential in the system.

As you have seen, an agroecosystem is one that has been radically simplified by humans, who must then take over responsibility for many of the functions once performed naturally. This includes building in redundancy.

■ What were the strategies in pre-colonial Indian and late imperial Chinese systems that might be thought of as building redundancy into the agricultural system?

☐ The strategies included stockpiling surpluses (Figure 3.13), storing water in irrigation systems and keeping land in common (assuming the land was not intensively used).

■ What do you think the effect of aggressive incorporation into global markets was on these kinds of in-built redundancy?

☐ Generally, uncommitted potentiality in the system seems to have been converted into productive use, wherever possible. This seems to have contributed in a major way to the vulnerability of these systems to both environmental and economic variability.

Figure 3.13 A traditional grain store in India.

One of the major challenges of governing an agricultural society, as you saw above, is managing the swings between surplus and shortfall by building redundancy into the system. One of the criticisms that can be levelled at the British colonial administrators of India is that their governance, in this regard, was hugely inappropriate.

■ Recalling what was said in Chapter 2 about the implications of long-distance migration, why would the British have been ill-prepared to govern monsoonal Asia?

☐ Most of their experience of climate and other environmental conditions came from temperate northwestern Europe, which is beyond the direct sphere of influence of monsoons and the most extreme effects of the ENSO.

By this logic, governance related to the handling of environmental uncertainty by Indian or Chinese rulers should be much better informed. Although the 'local' strategies for ameliorating the effects of drought and famine contrasted markedly with colonial tactics, we should be very careful not to give an overly flattering and uncritical picture of pre-colonial governance. There are good reasons to be sceptical of any claims that governance before colonial intervention was even-handed or universally effective.

■ Recalling what Chapter 2 said about 'steering' societies, how would you sum up the governance that was predominant in pre-colonial India and late imperial China – in two words?

☐ The evidence suggests that both the Chinese and the Indian administration of drought and famine was heavily 'top-down'.

■ What do you think the implications of this administration would have been with regard to the needs of 'ordinary' people at ground level?

☐ It should make us doubt whether the interests, knowledge and experiences of people 'on the ground' were taken into full consideration.

While village communities did play a part in managing environmental and economic uncertainty in traditional Asian social life, we need to be mindful of the limits of public participation in decision making, at the village level, and especially above this level. The economist Amartya Sen (2001) makes the point that traditional agricultural social systems typically fail to offer sufficient economic opportunities or protective arrangements for all members of society. These shortcomings, he suggests, are closely tied to the restrictions on participation at all levels of decision making. Sen refers to this as 'alienated governance' (Figure 3.14).

Figure 3.14   A painting of Emperor Aurangzeb, the Mughal Emperor of India from 1658 to 1707, being carried by his subjects.

It might be judicious, then, to view the attempts at famine mitigation in pre-colonial India and late imperial China as, at best, patchy and inconsistent. In many cases, the most effective precautions would have been taken at the 'grassroots' level: notably the growing of hardy 'famine crops' such as millet or sorghum.

In the case of traditional agricultural societies, China especially, we should also keep in mind that the historical recording of famine mortality – or lack of mortality – has been severely hampered by the incompleteness of data that follows from rural isolation.

However, as you have seen, the situation could get worse. The problem with British colonial governance was that it was even more alienated from the interests and needs of people 'on the ground'. Moreover, one of the main tasks that European colonial governors set themselves was the opening of peasant or traditional societies to the global market, based on a strong faith that the global market itself is a powerful self-regulating system.

But one of the lessons that might be learned from the tragedies of the colonial period is that markets, like many other complex systems, are subject to sudden and surprising shifts. And the effects of these shifts are far from evenly distributed.

Behind this vision of markets as 'self-regulating' is the assumption that they work as a kind of 'level playing field', in which all producers and all consumers have an equal say in 'steering' the system. But this is misleading. The 'playing field' is far from level because of the great differences in power and wealth between people who are drawn into markets. Those who have economic resources to fall back on are far more resilient in the face of downturns. Indeed, they can often profit from the vulnerability of smaller producers.

From an environmental point of view, there is a further reason why the level playing field of the global marketplace is a dangerous assumption.

■ Keeping the case of monsoonal India and China in mind, what is this reason?

☐ The extremes of climatic fluctuation and other forms of environmental variability interact with economic variables. This gives an added 'unevenness' to the surface of the global playing field.

This section focused on climatic fluctuations that affect countries in the monsoonal belt. This should not obscure the fact that vulnerability to climate change is also of vital importance for people living in temperate zones, as you will see in Book 3.

3.5   Global governance: obligations in a connected world

The tension between uneven real-world conditions and idealised visions of equality in the global market is no less important in the current era than it was over a century ago. Today, to an even greater extent than in the colonial 19th century, there are strong inducements for producers and consumers all around the world to participate fully in global markets. These markets are highly competitive, putting pressure on producers to bring the maximum amount of produce to the market at the minimum price. Across the world, this pressure is leading to intensification of agriculture and other forms of production (Figure 3.15a, b).

Figure 3.15   (a) Mechanised dredging to clear weeds in the Gezira canals, Sudan; (b) intensive cultivation in Gezira, Sudan.

However 'development' is perceived, the sort of economic efficiency that is promoted by competition in global markets must be part of the picture.

As you saw earlier in this chapter, the WRI sees the great challenge now confronting the world as one of understanding the vulnerabilities and resilience of ecosystems in order to reconcile them with the demands of development.

■   In the light of the factors that contribute to ecosystem resilience, and the competitive pressures of the global economy, is there a tension within WRI's challenge?

☐   Given that redundancy plays an important part in ecosystem resilience, the imperative of protecting ecosystems may pull in a different direction from the demands of development in the global economy. Remember that even plans for sustainable development have tended to assume further massive increases in levels of global economic activity (see Section 1.3.2).

The study of agricultural systems brings the issue of resilience and vulnerability in both ecological and economic systems into sharp focus. Clearly, we need to take the question much further.

Increasingly, over the past two centuries it has been not only agriculture but also **industrial production** that has channelled resources towards human consumption. Industry, and industrialised agriculture, takes the process of cutting out 'extraneous' loops and taking over ecosystem functions far further than peasant farmers could ever have imagined. The ultimate aim of industrial production is to place all aspects of the productive system under human control.

For a long time it was thought that the extended control over natural processes implicit in industrial production meant that industrial systems were immune to the vagaries of environmental variability that beset agroecosystems. The rising awareness of global environmental problems over recent decades reveals the flaws in this assumption.

This chapter has considered the question of ecosystem resilience and vulnerability on the local scale of the coral reef and at the regional level of the agroecosystem. In a similar way, we are now impelled to think about resilience and vulnerability on a global scale, as you will see in more detail later in the course.

The quest for sustainability is an attempt to steer the development of our societies on a course that leads away from ecological vulnerability and towards resilience. In this sense, to think about sustainability is to think also about governance: to consider all the processes by which we guide, manage and direct our societies.

Directing communal life in a way that keeps a local coral reef healthy and intact, as you saw, is quite a challenge. Administering an entire agricultural society creates a whole new set of demands. And you have seen what can happen when these demands are insufficiently met. Today, we have to think about governance at a global level, which presents a challenge of a scale and complexity that is without precedent.

How can we even contemplate steering the social life of an entire planet? We can draw some consolation from the fact that our understanding of complex systems is advancing steadily. And in many ways the question of governance (which shares its root in *kubernetes* with the word 'cybernetic') is about negotiating complex issues.

Today, it is becoming increasingly apparent that governance that does not involve a high degree of 'feedback' from throughout the social system – from the grassroots upwards – is likely to suffer from serious insufficiencies and imbalances.

This understanding resonates clearly with what we know about the working of complex systems. In particular, we recognise that such systems have properties that emerge from the interplay of all their elements – properties that cannot, therefore, be found at any single point in the system. By this reasoning, no individual, or even a cluster of individuals, can encompass the interests, the experiences, the learning of all the people who make up a social system. When we are dealing with any complex system, including a social system, a single 'helmsman' is, quite simply, not up to the task.

In case this makes governance sound like a purely technical problem, it is important to remember the extent of the suffering that can be caused by inappropriate responses to environmental and social change. Our growing understanding of the way in which large-scale climatic fluctuation shapes the lives of people around the globe is a reminder that there are forms of vulnerability that industrial control of the productive process cannot alleviate. This question of vulnerability takes a radical new turn once we acknowledge that industrial activity can exacerbate environmental extremes.

The gathering evidence of human-induced global environmental change raises profound issues about our obligations to other people who are distant in time and space. But this sort of ethical issue should not overshadow the possibility that we might also feel obligations towards people elsewhere on the planet who are threatened by quite natural environmental changes. As, indeed, they might feel responsibility for us.

'Obligation' comes from the Latin word *ligare*, which means to bind, and there are various ways in which our growing sense of ties and linkages to distant other people might affect the way we feel obligated to, or responsible for, each other, as you will see later in the course.

Just as we are increasingly aware that the processes of globalisation open up new links between people on different sides of the world, so too does our emerging understanding of the dynamics of global climate suggest that people from different regions are 'teleconnected' in previously unknown ways.

This sense of a world made up of intensive connectivity – both natural and anthropogenic – now impels us to consider the question of governance on a global scale. At the same time, another kind of interconnectivity may also be a condition of any sort of planet-scaled governance. Several centuries ago, shipping networks gave an intimation of global connectivity by weaving together insights from small islands strung across vast oceans. Today, new information and communications technologies offer novel possibilities for bringing together data and experience from every part of the world.

These possibilities raise an important question. Will these media reinforce top-down modes of control and market-driven pressures – or will they facilitate broad-based 'feedback' and participation in 'steering the globe'? There is no simple answer (at least not from 'inside' the system!) – but this is a question you may want to reconsider from time to time during the course.

3.6   Summary of Chapter 3

3.1   Human impacts can compound the stress caused by natural variability to induce catastrophic shifts in an ecosystem. These shifts often result in a much lower level of biodiversity.

3.2   Ecosystems belong to the category of complex systems, which means they have the potential to stabilise or to transform themselves in response to changing conditions. The tangled feedback loops that enable ecosystems and other complex systems to adjust also make it extremely difficult to predict future states of the system.

3.3   Preserving redundancy tends to be the best means of maintaining resilience in an ecosystem or other complex system.

3.4   Human hunting and gathering communities generally keep their demands on the biological productivity of ecosystems at a low level, which conserves ecosystem resilience.

3.5   The transition to agricultural production involves channelling a high proportion of biological production to human consumers and entails a significant simplification of ecosystems. This simplification tends to reduce natural resilience.

3.6   Agricultural societies must find ways to cope with the effects of seasonal and longer-term climatic variability if they are to endure. This means that famine prevention and relief is usually an important aspect of the governance of these societies.

3.7   The integration of traditional agricultural societies into global markets exposes peasant producers to the uncertainties of the global economic system, which can compound the uncertainties of climatic variability.

3.8   Top-down governance has limitations when it comes to responding to environmental and economic variability.

3.9   There is unevenness to global markets because of economic inequality and environmental variability around the planet. Global market pressures encourage the maximum development of resources, which can undermine resilience in economic and ecological systems.

3.10   Our growing understanding of global interconnections raises ethical questions about our obligations to other people who are distant in time and space, and underscores the need for governance on a global scale. Effective governance requires input and feedback from throughout the social system.

Questions for Chapter 3

Question 3.1

Which of the following statements about complex systems, if any, are true?

(a) They are open to inputs from outside the system.

(b) They have many components that are richly interconnected.

(c) They have many internal interconnections but no external connections.

(d) Their feedback loops make them much more stable than simple systems.

(e) They have feedback loops that enable them to adjust under
     changing conditions.

Question 3.2

An island community that depends on its coral reefs to attract tourists wants to develop its tourist industry in a sustainable way. As tourist numbers grow, the islanders monitor the relative areas of their coral reefs that are dominated by coral and dominated by macro-algae. They use the results as the main indicator of the sustainability of their tourist industry developments.

Do you think this is a wise strategy? In a maximum of 80 words, explain your answer.

Question 3.3

Which of the following, if any, are reasons why computer models of complex systems have limitations when predicting catastrophic shifts?

(a) Computer models are simulations that bear no relation to the real world.

(b) Computers are machines so they can only model simple systems
     without feedbacks.

(c) Computer models can deal with feedback but it is very difficult to find
     out what the multiple, entangled forms of feedback are that give rise to
     catastrophic shifts.

(d) It is very difficult to give values for all components and all feedbacks in
     the model.

(e) Knowing all components and all feedbacks doesn't help because catastrophic
     shifts are completely random events and are therefore totally unpredictable.

Question 3.4

Which of the following statements, if any, are good ways to look after an ecosystem we value?

(a) Minimise the human impacts that undermine resilience.

(b) Prevent all disturbance to the ecosystem.

(c) Reduce redundant aspects of the ecosystem so that it becomes more efficient.

(d) Maintain the diversity of functions and elements in the ecosystem even if they do not appear necessary.

Question 3.5

Which of the following statements, if any, are ecological implications of the shift from hunting and gathering to agricultural production?

(a) A much higher proportion of biological production is channelled to human beings.

(b) Humans add many new connections and components to the natural ecosystem.

(c) Agricultural technologies take over some of the functions once performed by natural ecosystems.

(d) The resilience of natural ecosystems can be severely compromised.

Question 3.6

Which of the following statements, if any, describe the climatic conditions of monsoonal Asia as they are now understood?

(a) The monsoon brings variation in rainfall between seasons and from year to year.

(b) The ENSO drives the monsoon system.

(c) The monsoon system drives the ENSO.

(d) The main influence of the ENSO on the monsoonal system occurs during phase-locking.

(e) Under the conditions of phase-locking, the effects of the ENSO and the monsoon system cancel each other out.

Question 3.7

Which of the following actions, if any, would be likely to contribute to the resilience of an agricultural society?

(a) Relying on market forces to distribute resources to the most needy people.

(b) Stockpiling foodstuffs during years of surplus.

(c) Maximising the use of land to provide an exportable surplus.

(d) Developing and maintaining irrigation systems that store water and regulate its flow.

(e) Tax increases during periods of adversity to pay for food imports.

(f) Tax relief or concessions during periods of adversity.

Question 3.8

In three to four short sentences, describe the likely effects of a phase-locking of a downturn in the global market with a period of extreme rain deficit on a late 19th-century farmer in India.

Question 3.9

Which of the following, if any, are examples of 'top-down' governance?

(a) Village-level management of common lands and irrigation systems.

(b) Government taxes on all cultivated land.

(c) Redistribution of foodstuffs from regions with a food surplus to regions with a food shortfall.

(d) National policies restricting food exports during periods of adversity.

(e) The decision by farmers to plant some of their land with drought-resistant crops.

(f) The decision by farmers to plant some of their land in crops for the global market.

Question 3.10

State two reasons why global markets might be viewed as operating on an uneven 'playing field', rather than a level one.

References

Davis, M. (2001) *Late Victorian Holocausts: El Niño Famines and the Making of the Third World*, London, Verso.

Kripalani, R.H. and Kulkarni, A. (1997) 'Climatic impact of El Niño/La Niña on the Indian monsoon: a new perspective', *Weather*, vol. 52, pp. 39–46.

Kurlansky, M. (1999) *Cod*, London, Verso.

Marten, G. (2001) *Human Ecology: Basic Concepts for Sustainable Development*, London, Earthscan.

Pauly, D.J., Christensen, V., Guenette, S., Pitcher, T.J., Sumaila, U.R., Walters, C.J., Watson, R. and Zeller, D. (2002) 'Towards sustainability in world fisheries', *Nature*, vol. 418, pp. 689–95.

Sen, A. (2001) 'Apocalypse then', *The New York Times* [online], www.nytimes.com/books/01/02/18/reviews/010218.18senlt.html (Accessed 2 February 2009).

Scheffer, M., Carpenter, S., Foley, J.A., Folke, C. and Walker, B. (2001) 'Catastrophic shifts in ecosystems', *Nature*, vol. 413, pp. 591–6.

World Resources Institute (WRI) (2000) *World Resources 2000–2001 People and Ecosystems: The Fraying Web of Life*, Washington, DC, WRI.

Chapter 4
Island Antarctica

4.1   Introduction

There is a long history of human interaction with island ecosystems. As you have seen, the arrival of people on any previously unsettled island has always been a risky venture because the island ecosystem and the incoming human social systems are inevitably new to each other. However, there is evidence to suggest that over time some human populations and island ecosystems have been relatively successful in adjusting to each other. We say 'relatively' because there is always a background of uncertainty in the form of natural variations – such as El Niño events – that may push the readjusted island ecosystem beyond its limits of tolerance. But social systems also have variations, such as economic downturns, which can also test tolerance levels. As you saw in Chapter 3, when crises in the realm of social life overlap with extremes of natural variation (Section 3.4), the result can be catastrophic in every sense. And this can occur not just on the scale of small islands but right across continents.

It is a challenge to understand how human interventions transform the natural world. This raises the issue of sustainability. However, it is even more of a challenge to come to terms with the way in which variable and unstable human social systems interact with variable and unstable natural systems. For this, the theme of sustainability needs to be complemented with the other course themes: uncertainty, governance and globalisation.

The rest of this book investigates one system in more detail. Antarctica, although vast, is really a continent-sized island surrounded by smaller islands. For the purposes of this book, it has one key advantage that is summed up very well by Edwin Mickleburgh:

> Less than a hundred years ago Antarctica still awaited the sound of a human voice, the imprint of a human boot. Two hundred years ago and no human eye had looked upon it. Antarctica was the object only of speculation which had absorbed philosophers and geographers alike since Aristotle first postulated the existence of a southern continent.

> (Mickleburgh, 1987)

Antarctica is a modern example of the interaction between humans and a 'pure' island ecosystem with subsequent human interaction. Although remote, the teleconnections between this region and the rest of the world are important. You have already seen one example of this in the belief of the Maldivian people that the possible collapse of the West Antarctic Ice Sheet could completely destroy their islands. This collapse could occur at the end of a set of complex feedback processes that make up the web of interconnections between Antarctica and the rest of the world. We need to understand the interactions between these feedbacks and their potential impacts in the future.

Here you will learn about the geography, ecosystem and development of Antarctica over the last 200 years. The physical environment and the ecosystem have much inherent natural uncertainty. Coping with this uncertainty has led to the development of a special system for dealing with globalisation and governance issues. But, like any international solution, Chapter 6 will show that this did not always produce the desired result.

Returning to the quotation above, you may have been surprised to read that the Greek philosopher Aristotle first thought there could be an unknown continent to the south. Greek astronomers named the star constellation above the North Pole *arktos*, meaning 'the bear'. The opposite end of the Earth, at the South Pole, was simply named *ant-arktos* because it was the opposite of the north. Over the years this developed into the name Antarctica.

What do you imagine when you think of Antarctica? Take a few moments to make a mental note of what immediately springs to mind. You probably thought along the lines of an icy hell, a place where nature rules, a land untouched by humans, the last wilderness, and so on. You might have thought of penguins, whales, Captain Scott and his colleagues pulling a sledge through a terrible storm, or beautiful sunsets (Figure 4.1). Aside from these obvious and stereotypical images, what is the 'truth' about Antarctica? One very famous polar explorer described Antarctica as 'more lonely than London' (Cherry-Garrard, 1922). Does this tie in with what came into your mind? As pointed out earlier in this book, where you are clearly influences how you see things.

Figure 4.1   Views of Antarctica.

So, what is Antarctica really like? What is its geography, its climate and its ecosystem? How much impact have humans already had? Who lives there, who owns the land and who even cares? There is much information about Antarctica on the internet. Some of this information will be similar to what you have already considered – after all, the Web reflects cultural influence. However, cultural influence has produced some surprising misconceptions about the region that persist despite extensive media coverage. (Later in the course you will study the effect of the media on environmental issues in more detail.) For example, it is often said that the temperatures in Antarctica can be below –80 °C, winds can be over 250 km per hour and it is a dark and freezing place. But how true is this and how can this common view be reconciled with the concerns of the Maldivian people about global warming and imminent ice-sheet collapse?

The internet is an opportunity to go beyond simple fact gathering because you can formulate and answer your own questions using information and data that are not available with such breadth and ease from any other source. You will learn to develop this approach throughout your study of *The environmental web*. This chapter begins by looking at the 'discovery' of Antarctica. The motivation for any geographical journey is either exploration or exploitation, and the discovery of Antarctica was no different. So, you can see at once the role played by globalisation and sustainability. A discussion about sustainability should also implicitly consider the governance of the resource being exploited.

4.2 Early 'discoveries' of Antarctica

Although Aristotle's ideas turned out to be correct, they were not confirmed for many centuries. Western maps of the 16th century show an outline of this supposed 'land' – but there was no proof of its existence. After the outline of 'Antarctica' first appeared on a map, its presence was propagated through successive maps, as described in Box 4.1.

Box 4.1 Lost islands

Once land appears on a map, it is very difficult to remove it because deletion requires proof that the land is *not* there. Unfortunately, throughout most of human history, navigation has been a very imprecise science. A sea captain discovering land would mark it on a map, but the ship could have been hundreds of miles away from where it was thought to be in relation to 'known' land. Navigation was not improved until Captain James Cook (1728–1779) circumnavigated the Earth in the late 18th century using a chronometer, and precise navigation only become common in the late 19th century as the price of chronometers fell and they became commonly available.

An example of this imprecise marine navigation is shown in Figure 4.2, where all the islands in the South Atlantic Ocean that were removed when a 'new' British Admiralty chart was drawn in 1808 are shown in red. The oceanographer Henry Stommel researched this chart and tracked down the history of each of these 'lost islands' (Stommel, 1984). For example, he found papers suggesting that the island of Grande, which was 'discovered' by Antonio de la Roche in 1675, was actually an isolated headland on the coast of South America – about 2000 km away. In the Antarctic, with ice, poor weather and cloud obscuring the visibility of the skies, navigation problems were greatly increased.

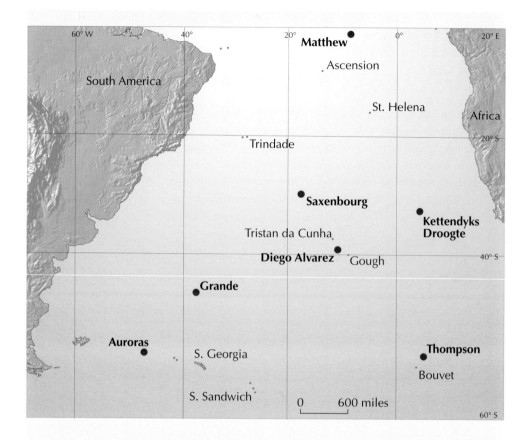

Figure 4.2 Map of the islands removed from a British Admiralty map of the South Atlantic Ocean in 1808.

Soon this 'Antarctic' land was appearing on western maps with the name *Terra Australis Incognito*. As more sailors ventured south, gaps in geographical knowledge were filled. For example, in 1578 Francis Drake (1540–1596) sailed through what became the Drake Passage and conclusively proved that any possible *Terra Australis Incognito* was not connected to South America. As usual, however, the western notion of historical discovery and exploration is not the whole story. In Chapter 2 you saw how 18th-century European sailors 'discovered' already inhabited islands. In fact, the first known Antarctic polar observations are from a Polynesian oral legend from the island of Rarotonga (Cook Islands). They tell of a chief called Ui-te-Rangiora who sailed to the Southern Ocean in an ocean-going canoe around AD 650 and found ice and snow. Another Polynesian from the Cook Islands called Aru-Tanga-Nuku is said to have repeated this amazing voyage around AD 800.

The first 'positive' evidence for the discovery of Antarctica though, is from Captain James Cook who famously circumnavigated the globe twice before dying on his third voyage. Cook also recorded possible regions for exploitation. On his second voyage, his two ships, *Resolution* and *Adventure*, crossed the Antarctic

Circle (66.5° S) in January 1773. They soon ran into an impenetrable wall of sea ice and Cook wrote in his journal that:

> The ice was so thick and close that we could proceed no further … I could see nothing to the southward but ice, in the whole extent from east to WSW without the least appearance of any partition.

(quoted in Hough, 1994)

Cook crossed the Antarctic Circle on two further occasions but, despite sailing a long way south, he never found an Antarctic continent. However, he had begun discovering the islands around Antarctica. While following up various leads from another sea captain, one of Cook's officers wrote in his journal:

> We've been for these six or seven days past cruising for the land the Frenchman gave intelligence of at the Cape of Good Hope … if my friend Monsieur found any land, he's been confoundedly out in the latitude and longitude of it all, we've searched the spot he represented it being and its environs too pretty narrowly and the devil an inch of land is there …

(quoted in Hough, 1994)

Some of the islands Cook was looking for did exist though. Although de la Roche is credited with being mistaken about Grande island, he is also credited with the first sighting of the island of South Georgia in 1675 (although this too may have been a case of mistaken identity). Cook made the first recorded landing in January 1775 and he promptly claimed it for the King with 'a descharge [*sic*] of small arms'. He did not like it and described it as 'savage and horrible'. However, he did think he had discovered *Terra Australis Incognito* – the problem was that it was not the resource-rich area that they had hoped for. He wrote 'not a tree or shrub was to be seen, no not even big enough to make a toothpick' (quoted in Hough, 1994).

Cook began to survey the coastline and soon determined that South Georgia was only an island and he wrote:

> This land which we had taken to be part of a great continent was no more than an island of 70 leagues in circuit … Who would have thought that an island of no greater extent than this is situated between the latitude of 54° and 55° should in the very height of summer be in a manner wholly covered many fathoms deep with frozen snow …

(quoted in Hough, 1994)

He left South Georgia in a southeast direction and discovered the South Sandwich Islands (which you will hear more of later). As *Resolution* and *Adventure* subsequently headed north, Cook was convinced that if there was an Antarctic continent it was to the south of a wall of **pack ice** and, if found, it would also be covered in ice and snow and be a desolate place. In his private journal, he wrote that if anyone were to discover such a land 'I make bold to declare that the world will derive no benefit from it'. Although Cook did not seem to consider South Georgia to be the resource-rich area he had hoped for, he did write 'Seals or Sea Bears were pretty numerous ... the shores swarm'd with young cubs' (quoted in Hough, 1994).

So, after discovery came exploitation.

4.3   The discovery of 'real' Antarctica

Cook's naturalists were well aware that there were many other areas in the Southern Ocean with large seal populations. But perhaps they did not understand how quickly these stocks would be overexploited and then crash. With the potential to obtain huge fortunes from sealing, the exploitation began in earnest. British and American sealers initially said that people could not land on the island of South Georgia without first killing seals. In 1825, the English sealer and explorer James Weddell (1787–1834) calculated that 1 200 000 sealskins had been taken from South Georgia alone.

■   Do you think it would have been possible to exploit the seals in a sustainable way once they were discovered?

☐   The key course theme of sustainability is about exploiting a system without undermining it. Without knowledge of the natural cycles of seal populations or the uncertainty in the ecosystem, exploitation would not have been any more sustainable than the examples you have already encountered.

Weddell had a good idea about what sustainability meant and he was saddened by this slaughter. He wrote that a sustainable harvest of skins would have allowed up to 100 000 seals being taken for many years to come but, by taking too many, the sealers had destroyed everything. The seal population first faltered and then collapsed. As South Georgia and other islands were stripped of their seal populations, the sealers had to move further and further southwards to find unexploited islands where profits would remain high. It is very difficult to piece together the exploration and exploitation activities during this period because records of ships' movements were of course commercially valuable, and captains went to great lengths to make sure that their voyages were kept secret from competitors. What is certain is that in the next 20 years or so, Antarctica was 'discovered'. What is rather more uncertain is *who* discovered it.

The British view is that the English sea captain William Smith (b. 1775) sighted land first. He was sailing in the brig *Williams* on a voyage from Buenos Aires in Argentina to Valparaiso in Chile when he sighted the South Shetland Islands on 19 February 1819. In October of that year, Smith landed on King George Island and took possession for the King on 15 October. However, many have argued that the South Shetland Islands are not the Antarctic mainland. The Royal Navy then chartered the *Williams* with Edward Bransfield (1785–1852) in command and, on 30 January 1820, they sighted and charted Trinity Land, now the Trinity Peninsula and part of mainland Antarctica. Clearly 'delighted' at their good fortune, one of the crew wrote that the sight was 'a prospect the most gloomy that can be imagined' (Sullivan, 1957). So was Antarctica discovered by the British?

In fact, the Russian naval explorer Thaddeus Bellingshausen (1778–1852), with his ships *Vostok* and *Mirny*, had sighted land on 15 January 1820, but he was unable to reach it. So, Bransfield appears to have been beaten by a few days, although the Russian crew never landed.

However, it would be too easy if that was the whole story. The American view is that the sealer Nathaniel Palmer (1799–1877) discovered Antarctica. Palmer was in command of the sloop *Hero* and, at the end of January 1821, was sailing along the Antarctic Peninsula when fog descended. As the fog thinned he found himself worryingly between two large warships. Naturally, he ran up his Stars and Stripes flag and the warships responded by hoisting the Cross of St Andrew – the flag of imperial Russia. It was Bellingshausen again and he told Palmer that he had been beaten.

Clearly then, there is a British claim, a Russian claim and finally an American claim for the discovery of Antarctica. So, which is correct? And what about the Polynesian explorers? Indeed, by now you may even be thinking 'is this important?' It is important because Antarctica has rich resources and the discoverer of the region could legitimately lay claim to them – as indeed Europeans did previously in many other parts of the inhabited world.

So, who discovered Antarctica? It could be that it was none of these three 19th-century mariners. There were at least 50 sealing ships operating in the region at this time but, because of commercial priorities, they kept their location secret.

Once countries were aware of the 'limitless' resources, over the next 100 years a series of expeditions set out to discover the extent of this region. With poor equipment and only sailing ships, the people on these expeditions suffered terrible and famous hardships, and this period in polar history has become known as the 'heroic age'. Table 4.1 lists some of the key expeditions in this period, some of which have give us famous and enduring images of Antarctica, such as Shackleton's trapped ship *Endurance* (Figure 4.3).

Figure 4.3   Shackleton's ship *Endurance* trapped in the sea ice of the Weddell Sea (1915).

Table 4.1 Some of the key expeditions to Antarctica.

Year	Expedition
1773	Captain James Cook (British) crosses the Antarctic Circle
1820	Thaddeus Thaddevich Bellingshausen (Russian) makes the first sighting of the Antarctic continent
1820	Edward Bransfield (British) makes the first sighting of the Antarctic Peninsula
1821	Nathaniel Palmer (American) sights Palmers Land
1840	Jules Sebastian Dumont d'Urville (French) discovers Terre Adélie
1873	Edward Dallman leads the first German Antarctic Expedition
1897	Adrien de Gerlache leads the Belgian Antarctic Expedition on the ship *Belgica*
1901	Otto Nordenskjöld leads the Swedish South Polar Expedition on the ship *Antarctic*
1901	Captain Robert Falcon Scott leads the British National Antarctic Expedition on the ship *Discovery* and makes the first extensive inland journeys
1902	William Bruce leads the Scottish National Antarctic Expedition to the South Orkney Islands on the ship *Scotia*
1903	Jean Charcot leads the French Antarctic Expedition on the ship *Français*
1907	Ernest Shackleton leads the British Antarctic Expedition on the ship *Nimrod* and gets to within 108 miles of the South Pole
1910	Captain Scott leads the British Antarctic Expedition on the ship *Terra Nova*. He reaches the South Pole on 18 January 1912 but he and his four companions die on the return journey
1910	Roald Amundsen leads the Norwegian Antarctic Expedition on the ship *Fram* and reaches the South Pole on 14 December 1911
1910	Nobu Shirase leads the Japanese Antarctic Expedition on the ship *Kainan Maru*
1911	Wilhelm Filchner leads the German South Polar Expedition on the ship *Deutschland*
1911	Douglas Mawson leads the Australasian Antarctic Expedition on the ship *Aurora*
1914	Ernest Shackleton leads the Imperial Trans-Antarctic Expedition on the ship *Endurance*. His ship is crushed in the pack ice before reaching the continent but he manages to lead his men to safety after drifting with the sea ice for over a year

You have probably heard of some of the expeditions in Table 4.1 but there will also be some that may not be familiar, such as that of William Bruce (1867–1921) in 1902–4 with the ship *Scotia*. His Scottish National Antarctic Expedition was scientifically a great success. In the same way that the modern-day media trumpets 'bad' news, the same was true of the 20th century and so, like other successful expeditions to the Antarctic, this one is not well known.

During all of the heroic expeditions listed in Table 4.1, there were also numerous sealing and whaling voyages to the Antarctic. Most of them were secret but some were not.

■   What do you notice about the nationalities of the people listed in Table 4.1?

☐   The majority are from the colonial powers of the 19th century.

Most of the sealers and whalers also came from the countries listed in Table 4.1. For example, when Scott was trapped in Antarctica in 1901, the Dundee whaling ship *Morning* was sent to rescue him. In the same way that the rest of the world was being exploited by the colonial powers in the 19th century, Antarctica was also being exploited by these same colonial powers. The pressures of globalisation meant that the distribution of resources in Antarctica was, as usual, not equitable. Having briefly described the discovery of Antarctica, the next section turns to what these explorers and exploiters discovered.

4.4   Antarctic geography

4.4.1   Maps of Antarctica

The best starting point for an investigation into Antarctic geography is to examine an up-to-date map of Antarctica. You may think that 'up to date' is rather a strange phrase to use when talking about maps and geography, but you will find out that our uncertainty about Antarctica extends not only to the ecosystem but also to the shape of Antarctica itself.

Figure 4.4 shows a map of Antarctica downloaded from the internet in 2002. You should be able to find others on the internet that are similar and more recent. This type of map is called a **polar projection** and is probably unfamiliar to you. Imagine looking at the Earth from a point in space directly over the South Pole. The continent would be stretched over the shape of the Earth with the South Pole at the centre. Then, if the outline of the continent was lifted from the Earth and flattened onto a piece of paper, the result would be the outline shown in Figure 4.4. Many maps (e.g. an Ordnance Survey map of Britain) are **Mercator projections** in which lines of latitude (distance from the Equator) run along the horizontal axis, and lines of longitude (the distance from the 'Prime Meridian' at 0° that runs north–south through Greenwich, England) run along the vertical axis. In a polar projection, lines of equal latitude are shown as concentric circles expanding from the centre of the map. The largest complete circle in Figure 4.4 is the latitude line of 50° S.

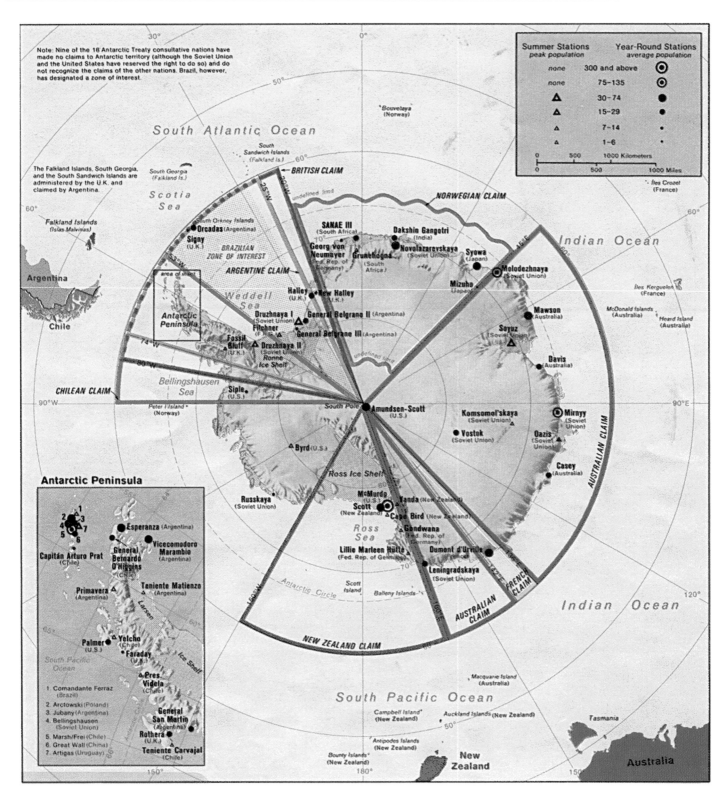

Figure 4.4   Map of the Antarctic downloaded from the internet (CARA, 2002).

■ As the circles get smaller, how do the latitude and the distance from the Equator change?

☐ Both the latitude and the distance from the Equator increase.

At the centre of the map, the South Pole is at 90° S and the latitude 'circle' is, of course, a dot. Lines of longitude on a polar projection are shown as radii that expand from the centre. At the top of the map is the 0° meridian and then, moving clockwise around the map, 90° E is at 3 o'clock, 180° E (or 180° W) is at 6 o'clock and 90° W is at 9 o'clock.

■ Maps often have an arrow on them pointing north. Why doesn't the map in Figure 4.4 have one?

☐ There is no single direction that is 'north' on this map because whichever direction you move in from the South Pole, you go north. Therefore, it is impossible to represent the direction of north with a single arrow.

There are numerous other ways of 'projecting' maps, apart from a Mercator projection or a polar projection. One feature you can see in Figure 4.4 is that Antarctica is roughly circular in shape. The only major exception to this is at approximately 60° W (about 10 o'clock) where a finger of land extends northwards. This finger of land is called the Antarctic Peninsula and, in Chapter 6, you will see that it has a special place in Antarctic governance.

■ Do you recognise any of the place names in Figure 4.4?

☐ There are some regions and places named after the people in Table 4.1.

If you are not very familiar with a polar plot it may be difficult to estimate how large the Antarctic is when compared with other, more familiar, continents. Figure 4.5 shows the outline of Antarctica overlaid on an outline of Europe drawn to the same scale, revealing that Antarctica is quite large – at least as big as Europe.

Can a map of Antarctica tell us anything about the current governance? If you look in detail at this continent, Figure 4.4 has many coloured radii extending from the South Pole that divide the continent up into pie-shaped segments. Each of the segments bounded by a different colour is labelled as a 'claim'.

Figure 4.5   The outline of Antarctica overlaid on a shaded map of Europe drawn to the same scale.

■ Are all of the segments bounded by a different colour discrete, or do some of them overlap?

☐ Some segments overlap at the Antarctic Peninsula.

What this might mean is discussed below but, for now, a simpler region bounded by only one pair of coloured radii is investigated. From 45° E to 136° E there is an area bounded by green lines and labelled 'Australian Claim'. This area contains land that is claimed by the Australian Government as Australian territory, and in Figure 4.4 there are several places within this region marked with a black dot or triangle. On a map of another part of the world, such dots might represent towns or cities, but here they are research stations. If you concentrate specifically on the region claimed by Australia, you can see that some of the black dots and triangles, such as Casey, have 'Australia' next to them in brackets. However, you can also see Vostok and several other stations with 'Soviet Union' in brackets within this 'Australian Claim'.

■ What do you think is the relevance of the country name?

☐ The country given in brackets is the country that operates the research station.

Consequently, within the Australian Antarctic Territory, there are research stations that have been built and are operated by the Soviet Union. This may seem strange. If the Australian Antarctic Territory has the same legal status as other Australian Territory, it is the equivalent of the Soviet Union building a research base in, for example, Tasmania. Antarctica must have some special legal status that allows countries to build scientific bases within regions 'claimed' by others.

■ Why is it odd that, according to this map, the Soviet Union has bases in the Antarctic?

☐ The Soviet Union has not existed as such since it was divided into individual states in 1990.

Clearly, this is yet another example of why you have to be careful of material on the Web.

■ Looking closely at the Australian segment, what else do you notice about the way the research stations are located?

☐ Nearly all of the stations are on the edge of the Antarctic continent. There are very few stations away from the coast.

In fact, when looking at the entire map, almost all of the stations are on the coast. Could this be telling us something about the geography and climate of Antarctica and the nature of scientific research there?

If you look again at Figure 4.4, and the regions claimed by different countries, what else strikes you as unusual when you look at which countries have made territorial claims? Australia, New Zealand, Chile and Argentina are relatively close to Antarctica and claims by them are not surprising. But why should countries such as France, Norway and Britain claim parts of Antarctica when they are so far away? In contrast, others such as the Soviet Union (now Russia and the Ukraine), the USA, South Africa, India, Japan and Germany have apparently not claimed territory in Antarctica. Chapter 6 will show that countries operating research stations in Antarctica are not all shown in Figure 4.4. There are many others, such as Korea, China, Sweden, Italy and Poland, that have also not made territorial claims. What can all this mean?

The simple map from the internet in Figure 4.4 has clearly opened up some very interesting questions about the governance of Antarctica and its globalisation, as well as the operation of scientific research there.

4.4.2   Facts about Antarctica

Figure 4.4 indicates that the governance of Antarctica is unusual. To learn more, the problem can be approached in a different way. There are many resources on the Web that give useful information about the countries of the world. One of the simplest approaches is to investigate the World Flag Database website, which lists some very basic 'facts' about each country. According to this site, in 2009 Antarctica apparently had: the status of a 'Continent', rather than that of a specific country; an area of 15 500 000 km^2; a capital city at the Amundsen–Scott Base at the South Pole; and its spoken languages were English, French, Norwegian and Spanish.

■   Is this last 'fact' concerning language likely to be true?

☐   No. If it were, it would mean that all the other people working in Antarctica and thus constituting part of its population, such as the Chinese, Indian and Polish scientists, do not speak their own language in the research stations run by their respective countries. Clearly, the statement is a generalisation, and Chinese dialects, Hindi and Polish, for example, are obviously spoken in this international territory.

The World Flag Database cannot be considered a reliable source for detailed information. Instead another source can be used that has an established reputation for being more reliable than this simple World Flag Database. The United States Central Intelligence Agency – more commonly known as the CIA – publishes a book called *The World Factbook* as an easily available central reference of data on each country in the world. Designed for government use, it is well researched and, although not presented in a very exciting way, it is reasonably reliable and frequently updated. It is also available online (*CIA World Factbook*). The information is presented in a standard format, but there is relatively little guidance about what these facts mean, or how to interpret them. Using this website, the main points are illustrated using the data that are given under the same headings for every country; consequently, you should not expect all of these headings to contain very useful information for Antarctica.

Box 4.2 shows some of *The World Factbook* information available for Antarctica in early 2009 (this data may differ slightly from what you see when you access this website). You already know from Figure 4.4 that several countries have set up year-round research stations. There is also some further information that might help to explain why, for example, Russia has a base in Australian Antarctic Territory.

■   What information is this?

☐   The part that says 'Seven [countries] have made territorial claims, but not all countries recognize these claims. In order to form a legal framework for the activities of nations on the continent, an Antarctic Treaty was negotiated that neither denies nor gives recognition to existing territorial claims; signed in 1959, it entered into force in 1961'. In effect, Russia could build its base because it does not recognise the Australian Antarctic Territory.

You can now see that the internet allows you to answer easy questions very quickly. For example, you can find a map to answer the question 'What shape is Antarctica?' and you can discover that apparently nobody owns Antarctica. But clearly it does not help with very difficult questions such as 'Why would a country go to the trouble of claiming part of Antarctica if no other country will recognise the claim?' Chapter 6 addresses the way this system of governance has evolved.

Now is a good time to do the website activities associated with this part of the chapter.

Box 4.2 Some details about Antarctica from *The World Factbook* (CIA, 2009)

Background

Speculation over the existence of a 'southern land' was not confirmed until the early 1820s when British and American commercial operators and British and Russian national expeditions began exploring the Peninsula region and areas south of the Antarctic Circle. Not until 1838 was it established that Antarctica was indeed a continent and not just a group of islands. Following World War II, there was an upsurge in scientific research on the continent. A number of countries have set up a range of year-round and seasonal stations, camps and refuges to support scientific research in Antarctica. Seven have made territorial claims, but not all countries recognise these claims. In order to form a legal framework for the activities of nations on the continent, an Antarctic Treaty was negotiated that neither denies nor gives recognition to existing territorial claims; signed in 1959, it entered into force in 1961.

Population

No indigenous inhabitants, but there are both permanent and summer-only staffed research stations. In all, 28 nations, all signatory to the Antarctic Treaty, operate through their National Antarctic Program a number of seasonal-only (summer) and year-round research stations on the continent and its nearby islands south of 60 degrees south latitude (the region covered by the Antarctic Treaty); these stations' population of persons doing and supporting science or engaged in the management and protection of the Antarctic region varies from approximately 4000 in summer to 1000 in winter; in addition, approximately 1000 personnel, including ship's crew and scientists doing onboard research, are typically present in the waters of the treaty region …

Geography

Location: continent mostly south of the Antarctic Circle

*Geographic coordinate*s: 90 00° S, 0 00° E

Map references: Antarctic Region

Area: total: 14 million km^2

land: 14 million km^2 (280 000 km^2 ice-free, 13.72 million km^2 ice-covered) (est.)

note: fifth-largest continent, following Asia, Africa, North America, and South America, but larger than Australia and the subcontinent of Europe

Area – comparative: slightly less than 1.5 times the size of the US

Land boundaries: 0 km

note: see entry on Disputes – international [on CIA World Factbook website].

Coastline: 17 968 km

Maritime claims: Australia, Chile, and Argentina claim Exclusive Economic Zone (EEZ) rights or similar to 200 nautical miles seaward from their continental claims, but like the claims themselves, these zones are not accepted by other countries; 21 out of 28 Antarctic consultative nations have made no claims to Antarctic territory (although Russia and the US have reserved the right to do so) and do not recognize the claims of the other nations; also see the Disputes – international entry [on CIA World Factbook website].

Climate: severe low temperatures vary with latitude, elevation, and distance from the ocean; East Antarctica is colder than West Antarctica because of its higher elevation; Antarctic Peninsula has the most moderate climate; higher temperatures occur in January along the coast and average slightly below freezing.

Terrain: about 98% thick continental ice-sheet and 2% barren rock, with average elevations between 2000 and 4000 meters; mountain ranges up to nearly 5000 meters; ice-free coastal areas include parts of southern Victoria Land, Wilkes Land, the Antarctic Peninsula area, and parts of Ross Island on McMurdo Sound; glaciers form ice shelves along about half of the coastline, and floating ice shelves constitute 11% of the area of the continent.

Elevation extremes: lowest point: Bentley Subglacial Trench – 2555 m

highest point: Vinson Massif 4897 m

Note: the lowest known land point in Antarctica is hidden in the Bentley Subglacial Trench; at its surface is the deepest ice yet discovered and the world's lowest elevation not under seawater.

Natural resources: iron ore, chromium, copper, gold, nickel, platinum and other minerals, and coal and hydrocarbons have been found in small uncommercial quantities; none presently exploited; krill, finfish, and crab have been taken by commercial fisheries.

Land use:

arable land: 0%

permanent crops: 0%

forests and woodland: 0%

other: 100% (ice 98%, barren rock 2%) (2005)

Natural hazards: katabatic (gravity-driven) winds blow coastward from the high interior; frequent blizzards form near the foot of the plateau; cyclonic storms form over the ocean and move clockwise along the coast; volcanism on Deception Island and isolated areas of West Antarctica; other seismic activity rare and weak; large icebergs may calve from ice shelf.

Environment – current issues: in 1998, NASA satellite data showed that the Antarctic ozone hole was the largest on record, covering 27 million square kilometers; researchers in 1997 found that increased ultraviolet light passing through the hole damages the DNA of icefish, an Antarctic fish lacking hemoglobin; ozone depletion earlier was shown to harm one-celled Antarctic marine plants; in 2002, significant areas of ice shelves disintegrated in response to regional warming.

Geography – note: the coldest, windiest, highest (on average), and driest continent; during summer, more solar radiation reaches the surface at the South Pole than is received at the Equator in an equivalent period; mostly uninhabitable.

Before moving on, look at the 'Geography' section in Box 4.2. The fourth entry gives the area of Antarctica as 14 million km², of which 280 000 km² is ice-free and the remaining 13.72 million km² are covered in ice. There is also a note saying that Antarctica is the fifth largest continent on Earth. This all sounds like very useful information. However, look back at the information about Antarctica from the World Flag Database.

■ What figure did it give for the area of Antarctica?

☐ The area of Antarctica is given as 15 500 000 km².

■ How does this compare with the area given by *The World Factbook*?

☐ There is a difference of 1 500 000 km².

This difference in area is over six times the total area of the UK. So which source should you believe? You may think that *The World Factbook* entry is more reliable, although you don't know where their information came from either. Clearly finding out 'facts' about Antarctica is going to be much harder than you perhaps imagined. With such an obvious discrepancy, can the other entries in the 'Geography' section of *The World Factbook* be trusted? You are probably safe in assuming that Antarctica really is the fifth largest continent, but how useful is that? The 'Climate' entry consists of some rather general statements, while the 'Terrain' and 'Elevation extremes' entries are a little more detailed, listing for example ice-free areas of coast and giving figures for average elevation, the highest mountains, the lowest point and the percentage of bare rock. There are also many interesting facts: for example, Antarctica has the lowest elevation on the Earth that is not under seawater – the Bentley Subglacial Trench which is an extraordinary 2555 m below sea level. The 'Natural resources' entry lists several resources, but in quantities said to be 'uncommercial', with none being presently exploited. It also says that there has been commercial fishing. The 'Land use' entry puts the continent entirely in a category called 'other'.

■ What does 'other' mean in this context?

☐ The land consists entirely of something other than arable land, permanent crops, permanent pasture, or forests and woodlands.

There then follows a list of various natural hazards such as blizzards, volcanoes and icebergs, and then a piece identifying the Antarctic 'ozone hole' and the disintegration of ice shelves surrounding the continent as the most important current environmental issues in the region. The last note says that Antarctica is the 'coldest', 'windiest', 'highest' and 'driest continent', and that 'during summer, more solar radiation reaches the surface at the South Pole than is received at the Equator in an equivalent period'.

It is difficult to interpret what the authors of *The World Factbook* mean by this last statement, but it certainly sounds surprising and is considered later. Finally, note that Antarctica is 'mostly uninhabitable'.

Going to the internet has produced 'facts', but what do they mean? The real issue is what have you learned about Antarctica from this 'reputable' source? Has it changed any of your perceptions, and which were possibly illustrated by the images in Figure 4.1? There is serious doubt about the accuracy of at least one of the facts – the area of Antarctica. So, can you rely on the other facts? There are many statements that are practically impossible to contradict. But again, return to the real question: have you learned anything about Antarctica from this source? Broadly speaking, if you know where to look, it would appear you can use the internet to answer relatively easy questions such as 'How high is the highest mountain in Antarctica?', but it is much harder to answer complex questions such as 'Why do two internet sites give different information on something as straightforward as the area of Antarctica?'

■   Give two reasons why the figures for the area of Antarctica are different.

☐   Both figures could be wrong – you cannot tell without seeing the sources of the data. Also both numbers could have been correct *when they were published*, e.g. the larger number could have been the area of Antarctica before a large ice shelf broke off and reduced the area to the smaller number.

Figure 4.6   A satellite photograph of Larsen-B Ice Shelf in 2008, showing the retreat of the edge of the shelf since 1995.

The second reason is plausible. Although a difference of six times the area of Britain sounds a lot, large chunks of ice shelf break off from Antarctica relatively frequently. For example, in 2000, a giant iceberg measuring 6800 km^2 broke off from an ice shelf and started drifting northwards away from Antarctica; and in 2002 about 3200 km^2 of the Larsen-B Ice Shelf on the eastern side of the Antarctic Peninsula spectacularly detached and broke up in only 35 days (Figure 4.6).

Statements on an internet site have the same problems as any unreferenced source. It is not possible to know if they are true, false or true at a particular time; in addition, when facts do change, some sites are updated more frequently than others. An added problem of the Web is the ease of access to information. The temptation is to use the first source found, without justification. This simple example of a relatively straightforward 'fact' about Antarctica (the land area) should have demonstrated the seriousness of this potential problem.

So far, you have found out quite a lot about Antarctica. However, if you want to use the internet in a different and more advanced way, you need to do some planning first. The next section introduces a scheme to help focus your efforts.

4.5   A short interlude – using the internet for research

Answers to straightforward questions such as 'What is the shape of Antarctica?' are quick and simple. However, one of the wonders of the internet is that it is possible to go much further than this. You can access *raw* data, carry out your own analysis, and draw appropriate conclusions. Although this is going much further than many people who use the internet, later in the course you will see that this method of working is very similar to how, for example, a journalist or scientist would do research. To be really efficient of course, you should never sit down at a computer until you know what you 'don't know'. Or, to put it another way, first you need to define a question. Questions such as 'Why is there a Russian base in Australian Antarctic Territory?' require more forethought than straightforward ones. To help you with these more difficult questions, you can follow the series of steps in Figure 4.7.

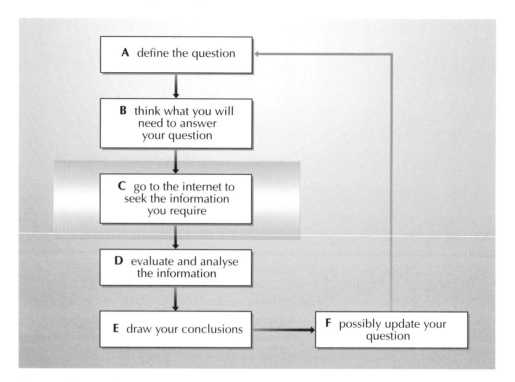

Figure 4.7   Schematic outline of a process for using the internet to answer a question.

Once you have chosen a question to ask, you should think carefully about the sort of information you would need to answer it. For example, imagine you are an engineer and have been asked to build a bridge across a river.

■   What sort of information would you need before building the bridge?

☐   You would need to know: how wide the river is, what load the bridge is to take, the depth of the river, and so on.

An engineer starts with the specification for the job. However, as you have come to appreciate, the difficult nature of environmental questions requires a strict specification. If your aim is to convince someone in another part of the world that they should change their lifestyle to help you, you need to be precise about what they will gain as a result. So, in Figure 4.7, Box A is relatively easy. The real problem will always be Box B: specifying what you need. Once you have this, Box C – the step that is online – will be focused and relatively short.

When you have found your information, you must *evaluate* it and then, finally, in Box E, draw your conclusions. Once you have answered even a simple question, you can follow the arrow to Box F and update your question to further your understanding. The key point is to use the internet in short, focused bursts rather than becoming sidetracked (step C). The more specific you are about the sort of information you intend to recover, and how you will then analyse it, the more successful your search will be. Overall, it means that you can be much more effective during your time spent online. You may find it helpful to refer back to Figure 4.7 until you have learned this, or found a similarly effective way of working online.

The geography part of *The World Factbook* entry (see Box 4.2) states that there are 'severe low temperatures' in Antarctica. In the next section, you will follow the process in Figure 4.7 to find out what the climate of Antarctica is like in this 'cold and frigid' place.

4.6   Antarctic climate

4.6.1   Air temperatures

What do you think of when you imagine the air temperatures of Antarctica? Low temperatures definitely, but how cold? Our perceptions are clouded by previous exposure to relevant information. In the case of Antarctica, many British people imagine Captain Scott dying on his return from the South Pole with his party suffering terribly (Figure 4.8). You may have seen wildlife programmes on television about the Emperor penguin, which hatches and brings up its chicks in the deep Antarctic midwinter (Figure 4.9). If so, you may agree with the English polar explorer Apsley Cherry-Garrard (1886–1959), who said 'Take it all in all, I do not believe anybody on Earth has a worse time than an Emperor penguin' (Cherry-Garrard, 1922).

Figure 4.8   Scott's party walking in a blizzard, sketched by Edward Wilson, one of the party who died with Scott.

Both images certainly suggest that conditions would be horrendous for humans. But is it like that all year round? For example, if you looked at mean air temperatures taken over a whole month for Britain, the 'normal' seasonal range would be from perhaps 3 °C to 18 °C. Would you expect a similar range of air temperatures in

Figure 4.9   An Emperor penguin (*Aptenodytes forsteri*) with its chick.

Antarctica? You may not even have imagined Antarctica as having different seasons, i.e. a winter, spring, summer and autumn. By following the scheme in Figure 4.7, you can use the internet to answer questions about Antarctic temperatures.

4.6.2   Mean temperatures across Antarctica

Figure 4.10 shows the mean temperatures for the southern summer and winter in Antarctica. The circular lines labelled −30, −20, 0, and so on, are in degrees Celsius and represent lines of equal temperature. These are called **isotherms**. If you look at the South Pole in Figure 4.10a, it lies between the −20 °C and the −30 °C isotherm. This means that the mean summer temperature at this location is between these two temperatures.

Now is a good time to do the website activities associated with this part of the chapter.

■ Assuming that the change in temperature between these two isotherms is linear – that is, it varies in proportion to the distance from them – estimate the temperature at the South Pole.

☐ The South Pole is closer to the −30 °C isotherm, so the mean summer temperature is probably about −28 °C.

The 0 °C degree temperature line circumscribes Antarctica in Figure 4.10a, and in some regions such as the Antarctic Peninsula, it is very close to the land. In other regions, such as the Weddell Sea and Ross Sea (see Figure 4.4), the 0 °C isotherm is a long way from land.

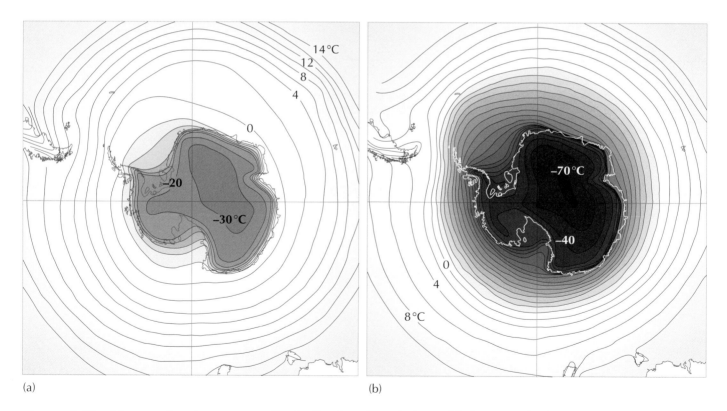

(a)   (b)

Figure 4.10   Mean surface temperatures for the Southern Hemisphere. (a) Summer: the isotherms are in 2 °C steps from 12 °C to −10 °C, and then in steps of 10 °C. (b) Winter: the isotherms are in 2 °C steps from 10 °C to 0 °C, 1 °C steps from 0 °C to −10 °C, 5 °C steps from −10 °C to −40 °C, and 10 °C steps from −40 °C to −70 °C.

■ Assume again that the temperature change between isotherms is linear. When isotherms are close together, is the temperature change with distance rapid or slow?

☐ It is rapid.

Where isotherms are widely spaced, the opposite is true and there is little variation in temperature over long distances. Looking at Figure 4.10a again, in the middle of the Weddell Sea you could move a few hundred kilometres towards the South Pole and the mean summer temperature would only change by about 2–3 °C. In contrast, at a longitude of 90° W, if you moved from the coast towards the South Pole by a similar distance, the temperature change could be as much as 20 °C. However, the mean summer temperature of most of the coast of Antarctica is about −2 °C.

The corresponding picture for the mean winter temperatures is very different (Figure 4.10b). The distance between isotherms is fairly constant from the −70 °C isotherm all the way out to the 0 °C isotherm (taking the varying steps between isotherms into account).

■ What is the mean winter temperature on the coast of Antarctica?

☐ About −10 to −15 °C.

From the coast out to the 0 °C isotherm, the change in mean surface winter temperature seems to be related to the distance from the coast. You can see that the Antarctic Peninsula does have some effect on the shape of these isotherms, as do the very large Filchner–Ronne and Ross Ice Shelves (see Figure 4.4 for the location of these areas; the Filchner Ice Shelf is continuous with and east of the Ronne Ice Shelf). Figure 4.10 shows clearly that the regions close to the sea have temperatures in quite a narrow range. In summer most of the Antarctic Peninsula is above 0 °C. Winter is more harsh on the coast but still no worse than some regions of the planet that are inhabited. In contrast, central Antarctica is very different.

You may be thinking by now that, as the 0 °C isotherm is out over the ocean, does this mean that the ocean freezes? The answer is yes, and this is discussed in Chapter 5. However, before that there is one more important feature of the Antarctic climate to be considered – the seasonal cycle.

4.6.3 The seasonal cycle of atmospheric temperature in Antarctica

Figure 4.11 shows the seasonal temperature cycle at Adelaide Island, now called Rothera Point (a research station operated by the British Antarctic Survey on the northwest coast of the Antarctic Peninsula) over a 2-year period from December 1964 to December 1966. These dates were chosen because they are in the middle of the temperature record.

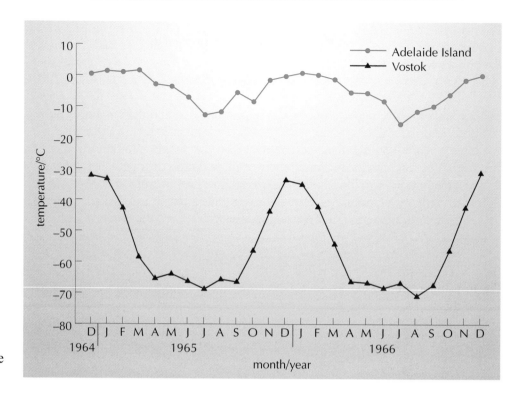

Figure 4.11 Seasonal atmospheric temperature cycle at the research stations Adelaide Island and Vostok.

■ Is the pattern (although not necessarily the actual temperatures) of the record for Adelaide Island in Figure 4.11 the same as you might expect in Britain?

☐ No, in the Southern Hemisphere the summer solstice is in December instead of June.

Thus there are warmer summer temperatures from December through to April, then a gradual fall during autumn down to minimum winter temperatures in June and July. In spring, temperatures rise slowly again to reach a maximum in the summer months. Broadly speaking, the record shows the same pattern in both years, with differences attributable to slightly different conditions in each year; for example, in 1966 there was a colder winter.

Figure 4.11 also shows the seasonal cycle at Vostok over the same period. Remember that Vostok is a research station operated by Russia deep inland on the Antarctic Plateau (see Figure 4.4). It has the distinction of being the place where the coldest temperature on Earth has been recorded (−89.2 °C). The question of why anyone would want to put a research station in such a savagely cold and remote place is addressed in Chapter 6. Comparing the seasonal cycle at Vostok with that at Adelaide Island shows striking differences.

■ What are the two main differences?

☐ In Vostok, summer is comparatively short, with a rapid rise in temperature followed by a rapid fall, and winter is long and cold, with temperatures approximately constant, showing no distinct minimum.

The absence of a distinct minimum winter temperature on the Antarctic Plateau has led to the winter being called a **coreless winter**. This is one of the major differences between the Antarctic continent away from the oceans, and the rest of the planet.

Surface temperatures are mainly determined by the amount of energy from the Sun (incident solar radiation) that actually reaches the Earth. The further away from the Equator you go, the less energy reaches the Earth's surface, and so temperatures are generally lower. You may already know that the Earth is inclined at approximately 23.5° to the Sun (Figure 4.12). In practice this means that, in the Antarctic winter, there is no incident solar radiation reaching the Earth south of 66.5° S at any time of day. North of 66.5° S there is only a very short day that increases in length the further north you go. At the tip of the Antarctic Peninsula during the winter solstice, there are only a few hours when the Sun is above the horizon. South of 66.5° S, as winter approaches and the Sun starts to disappear for longer each day, the atmosphere loses heat because there is less and less incident solar radiation to keep it warm. The ocean provides another source of heat that also affects atmospheric temperatures. In the same way that the water in a car radiator moves heat away from the engine, the ocean moves heat around the planet. During the Antarctic winter, the sea is relatively warm compared with the atmosphere and so acts as a source of heat for the coastal regions. However, inland the heat loss is so great that the temperature falls rapidly to effectively the lowest temperature it can reach. With no further cooling possible, and no source of heating either from the Sun or from the ocean, the temperature stays approximately constant, producing the coreless winter.

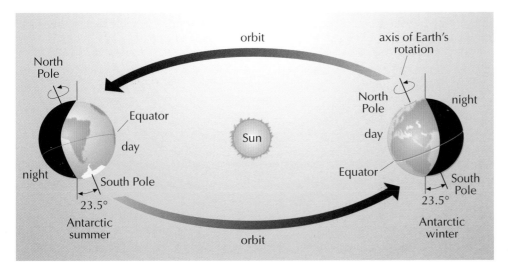

Figure 4.12 The Earth's orbit showing why the Antarctic is completely dark for part of the year.

In the Antarctic summer south of 66.5° S, Antarctica is continually illuminated by the Sun. Incident solar radiation is therefore at a maximum and temperatures rapidly rise as shown in Figure 4.11.

The World Factbook states that 'during summer, more solar radiation reaches the surface at the South Pole than is received at the Equator in an equivalent period'. You can see from Figure 4.12 why this is the case. At the Equator the Earth receives about 12 hours of sunlight per day constantly throughout the year. This can be compared with the 24 hours of sunlight the South Pole receives in summer. But as most of this energy is instantly reflected out to space by the snow and ice, it does not increase temperatures very much, and so the central Antarctic is still a hostile place.

It can be rather difficult to understand how the Earth orbits around the Sun, and which parts are in daylight and night-time in different seasons. Probably for this reason, clockmakers in the 17th and 18th centuries built mechanical models to show the orbits of the planets around the Sun. An **orrery** (Figure 4.13) is a beautiful piece of engineering and watching one work is a wonderful experience. The name 'orrery' comes from the second model ever made, which was for the Earl of Orrery in England. Most people are not rich enough to afford such a beautiful instrument but by searching for 'orrery', you can find digital alternatives on the internet, thus illustrating the fact that the internet is not merely a source of information; it can also help you understand that information.

Figure 4.13   The solar system model, or orrery, made by John Rowley of London for Charles Boyle, fourth Earl of Orrery, in 1712. The model shows the motions of the Earth and the Moon around the Sun.

4.7   How Antarctica became ice-covered

This chapter ends by explaining how Antarctica became ice-covered. You may know that the shape of the continents has not been constant throughout the 4.5 billion-year history of the Earth. The continents sit on plates that move around the planet over time. Going back in time to trace this continental drift, Antarctica was at 30° S (Figure 4.14a) at about 195 million years ago (195 Ma), and so mostly ice-free at that time. As the continent drifted southwards (Figure 4.14b), average temperatures decreased and precipitation began to turn to snow and settle on the land. This probably happened in the last 20 million years although we cannot be certain to within about 5 million years. Once snow began to settle, it reflected a greater amount of incident solar radiation out to space.

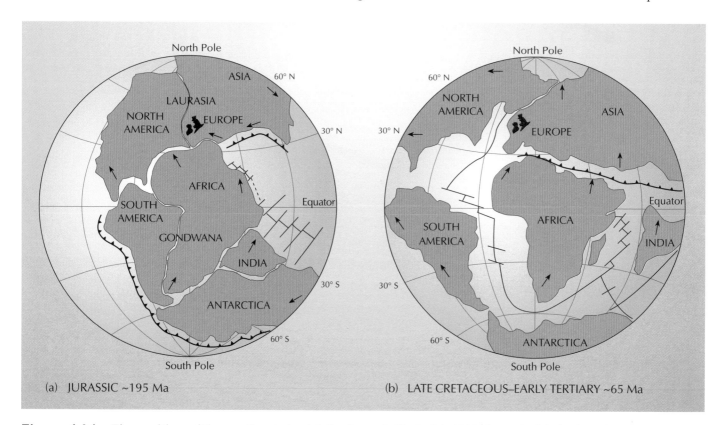

(a) JURASSIC ~195 Ma

(b) LATE CRETACEOUS–EARLY TERTIARY ~65 Ma

Figure 4.14   The position of the continents in: (a) the Jurassic Period (~195 Ma ago); (b) the late Cretaceous Period (~65 Ma ago).

■ What would have been the effect of reflecting more solar radiation out to space, rather than absorbing it?

☐ The heat from the solar radiation would have been lost and the continent would have cooled even more rapidly.

Even with a maximum incident solar radiation, the energy reaching the surface at high latitudes was far too low to raise air temperatures significantly.

As more and more snow fell on the continent, snow crystals on the bottom were crushed and turned into **glacial ice**. Over time, the Antarctic ice sheet has grown to a thickness of several kilometres that covers most of the continent today.

■ According to *The World Factbook* (Box 4.2), what percentage of Antarctica is covered by ice?

☐ It states that 98% of Antarctica is covered by ice (the remaining 2% being barren rock).

The ice sheet that covers Antarctica is derived from snow and so is freshwater. Between the ice crystals is trapped part of the Earth's atmosphere from the time when the snow fell. Later in the course, you will discover that by studying this ancient atmosphere, climate scientists have reconstructed a history of the planet going back almost half a million years. They have determined that the inclination of the Earth has not always been at 23.5° S to the Sun (as in Figure 4.12), but has varied over the millennia.

As snow continues to fall on the continent and is turned to ice, the weight of this ice causes it to flow away from the higher, central part of the continent, towards the edges, in slow-moving ice rivers called **glaciers** (Figure 4.15). When the glaciers reach the edge of the continent, they flow off the land into the ocean and break off to form **icebergs** (Figure 4.16). These icebergs, which are sometimes hundreds of metres thick, then drift with the ocean currents away from the continent. In some areas the ice from the glaciers does not break away and instead forms large, floating **ice shelves** (Figure 4.17), which are still attached to the continent. The largest ice shelves are the Filchner–Ronne Ice Shelf in the Weddell Sea and the Ross Ice Shelf in the Ross Sea (Figure 4.4). The Ross Ice Shelf was known as the 'Great Ice Barrier' in the 'heroic age' because most ice shelves appear as huge walls of ice rising up to 40 m above the ocean.

Figure 4.15   A typical glacier flowing down to the sea in an ice-carved valley.

Figure 4.16   An iceberg that has calved into the sea from a nearby glacier.

Figure 4.17   The edge of an ice shelf.

4.8   Conclusions

The discovery of Antarctica, although comparatively late in human history, was broadly similar to the discovery of other island systems such as Mauritius and St Helena: exploration was swiftly followed by exploitation. You have learned about the climate of Antarctica, but the implications of this knowledge go much deeper. If you were asked to find the mean temperature of Antarctica, could you now give a sensible answer? Later in the course, you will see that the idea of global mean temperature is critical to arguments about climate change. Regarding the Maldives and sea level, the ice shelves on the fringes of Antarctica are floating, and so displace the same weight of water as they contain. The collapse of part of the Larsen-B Ice Shelf, shown so dramatically in Figure 4.6, had no immediate effect on sea level. In contrast, the ice sheets that cover the continent are freshwater. If they melted these would provide *extra* water to the oceans and so raise sea level. The Maldivian people are quite right to be concerned about what may happen. These issues are covered in more detail later in the course.

The next two chapters consider the Antarctic ecosystem and how Antarctica was globalised. You will also see how the method of governance that has been developed is designed to cope with both sustainability and uncertainty.

4.9   Summary of Chapter 4

4.1 Human contact with the Antarctic is very recent. Once humans had discovered Antarctica, there was a rush of expeditions southwards from the 19th-century colonial powers.

4.2 Apart from the Antarctic Peninsula, Antarctica is roughly circular, centred approximately on the South Pole with an area about the same size as Europe. A polar projection map of the Antarctic is centred on the South Pole, with lines of longitude radiating from the pole and lines of latitude shown as concentric circles around the pole.

4.3 A Mercator projection map shows longitude as vertical lines and latitude as horizontal lines.

4.4 Several countries have made territorial claims in Antarctica but these are not recognised in International Law. Countries with territorial claims, plus several others, operate research stations in Antarctica, and these are mostly located on the coast.

4.5 The area of Antarctica is variable, depending on the area of ice shelf attached to it, and different figures for the total area are given by different sources. About 98% of the continent is covered by ice.

4.6 When using the internet to answer a question, it is possible to avoid distraction and minimise time online by posing a carefully considered and focused question, deciding in advance what information is needed to answer the question, then going offline to evaluate the information and draw conclusions.

4.7 Air temperatures in Antarctica depend on the amount of incident solar radiation received and the amount of heat gained from the ocean. Antarctica is often thought to have an extreme, unremittingly cold climate but, in fact, it has a seasonal climate, with relatively mild summers on the coast. Inland areas have a shorter summer and a coreless winter.

4.8 Antarctica was much closer to the Equator 195 million years ago, but continental drift has moved it to its present polar position. The thick sheet of glacial ice covering most of the continent probably developed within the last 20 million years. Glacial ice flows off the continent in glaciers and either remains attached to form a floating ice shelf or breaks off at the edges to form icebergs.

Questions for Chapter 4

Question 4.1

What are the main features of a coreless winter, and why would you not expect to see one on the coast of Antarctica?

Question 4.2

Why will the melting of an ice shelf not affect sea level?

Question 4.3

Who discovered Antarctica?

Question 4.4

Why would you not draw a map of Antarctica on a Mercator projection? What type of map projection would you use?

Question 4.5

Which of the following countries have *not* made a territorial claim in Antarctica but operate research stations? (a) Chile; (b) Argentina; (c) Australia; (d) the USA; (e) France; (f) Britain.

Question 4.6

Why does the area of Antarctica change over time?

Question 4.7

What would the climate of Antarctica have been like approximately 195 million years ago?

Question 4.8

Would you expect the warmest temperatures in Antarctica to be at the same time of year as those in Britain?

Question 4.9

What is the defining feature of glacial ice?

Question 4.10

Why should you be careful when looking for information on the internet?

Question 4.11

Why is thinking carefully about what you want to find on the internet desirable?

References

CARA (Center for Astrophysical Research in Antarctica) (2002) [online], http://astro.uchicago.edu/cara/vtour/ant.cia.gif (Accessed 2 February 2009).

Cherry-Garrard, A. (1922) *The Worst Journey in the World*, Constable and Co. Reprinted 1994, London, Macmillan.

CIA (2009) *The World Factbook* [online], www.cia.gov/library/publications/download/ (Accessed 13 May 2009).

Hough, R. (1994) *Captain James Cook*, London, Hodder and Stoughton.

Mickleburgh, E. (1987) *Beyond the Frozen Sea*, London, Paladin.

Stommel, H. (1984) *Lost Islands*, Vancouver, University of British Columbia Press.

Sullivan, W. (1957) *Quest for a Continent*, London, Secker & Warburg.

World Flag Database (2009) [online], www.flags.net/ (Accessed 4 February 2009).

Chapter 5
Perception and reality – the 'invisible' ecosystem

5.1   Introduction

If the motivation for the discovery of Antarctica in the 'heroic age' was well-publicised *exploration*, the voyages of *exploitation* that took place around the same time – for example, the voyages of the sealers – were, by contrast, generally hidden from view. This chapter looks at the ecosystem that these voyagers were exploiting to build up a picture of the true complexity of the natural environment. The Antarctic ecosystem is generally considered to be straightforward in that there are few animal species to consider. However, we need to understand what happens in this ecosystem in order to avoid repeating the events that happened on the islands of St Helena, Mauritius and Rapa Nui. Chapter 6 sets out the contemporary response to this question.

When you were asked to think about Antarctica in Chapter 4, did you consider the wildlife? It would not be surprising if you had, given the resources that media organisations such as the BBC have thrown at the region. What you may not have realised is that media organisations tend to focus on the 'charismatic macrofauna' – that is, the animals that are large, easy to observe and, of course, beautiful. In this chapter you will see that there is much more to the wildlife in Antarctica, and indeed in any region, than you may have realised. The aim here is to understand the marine ecosystem in Antarctica because this supports the region's biological resources. The feeding relationships among organisms in a given ecosystem is known as a **food web** and, in this chapter, you will see the contrast between the role played by large animals (macrofauna) at the top of the Antarctic food web, and the tiny ones (microfauna) at the bottom. The main components of the Antarctic ecosystem are invisible beneath the waves, and the smallest organisms are the most important.

Throughout this chapter the focus is on the key course theme of uncertainty in a natural system. The marine ecosystem is strongly influenced by the physical environment through processes that have a variety of time and space scales, from the turbulence and mixing caused by storms and ocean currents that act over periods ranging from days to years through to the thousands and millions of years of natural climate variations. But, as you saw earlier in this book, as well as being acted on by external forces such as turbulence, natural systems have their own inherent variability.

To understand how Antarctica's ecosystem has developed we must look at its habitats. In Chapter 4, you saw that Antarctica is an extreme environment. Although you may be aware that some species of wildlife are abundant, at least in some places, clearly, Antarctica does not exactly provide an obvious habitat for living things. Humans can inhabit a huge variety of places but we use technology to extend our range: for example, to go into space we need to take our environment with us in a space suit. Even so, much of Antarctica is at one extreme of the range of conditions where even adaptable humans can survive.

■ Recalling Chapter 4, what contrasting views of Antarctica as a habitat were described?

☐ On the one hand, Antarctica is a place where wildlife can be very abundant and diverse, for example with large penguin colonies. On the other hand, wildlife is sparse where the continent is covered with an ice sheet that is kilometres thick.

The contradiction between these two views of Antarctica as a habitat is resolved quite easily. The biologically rich picture is associated with the sea, the **marine ecosystem**; while the biologically poor picture is that of the land, the **terrestrial ecosystem**. This distinction is not rigid – both systems are variable – but it is a useful generalisation which underpins the development of this chapter.

5.2   The Southern Ocean

Have you heard of the Roaring Forties or the Screaming Fifties? They are the names given by the sailors to the winds that tear around the Southern Ocean. However, despite the extreme physical conditions, there really is plenty of life in the region. In Chapter 4 you saw a map of the atmospheric temperatures around Antarctica (Figure 4.10). Earth-orbiting satellites can show us the global sea surface temperature (SST) in much greater detail (Figure 5.1).

■ Large areas of the Southern Ocean in Figure 5.1 are coloured pink and purple. What do these colours indicate?

☐ Very cold surface temperatures. Mauve represents a temperature of ~4 °C, so the areas coloured pink are colder than this.

Figure 5.1   Map of global sea surface temperature. Different temperatures are shown as different colours and the range is from −2 °C to 32 °C. This image is the annual mean picture, but data for individual weeks can be downloaded from the internet. South Georgia is circled.

The boundary between the cold southern waters and warmer northern waters is called the **polar front**. South of the polar front, the SST only changes by about 4 °C all the way to the Antarctic continent, but to the north the SST increases very rapidly (from dark blue to green) by about 10 °C in a very short distance. The relatively uniform SST water south of the polar front makes up part of what is called the **Antarctic Circumpolar Current** (ACC). This current circulates in a clockwise direction around Antarctica and, although slow, the volume of water moving is tremendous – roughly 100 000 000 m^3 of water passes through the Drake Passage every second.

In Chapter 4, you learned that the ocean keeps the Antarctic coast relatively warm in winter (Section 4.6.3). However, it can also keep places cold. Captain Cook was surprised that South Georgia was covered in ice and snow when, at 54° S it is not so far from the Equator (Section 4.2) – after all, the British Isles are roughly the same distance from the Equator at 53° N and so both areas should receive roughly the same amount of solar radiation.

■ Looking at Figure 5.1, why do you think the island is so cold?

☐ South Georgia is south of the polar front and is surrounded by relatively cold water that affects the climate to such an extent that the island is almost as cold as the Antarctic itself.

If solar radiation were the only factor determining climate, South Georgia and the British Isles ought to be very similar, but clearly they are not. The Gulf Stream is a warm ocean current that originates in the Gulf of Mexico and travels northeast across the Atlantic. It flows past the British Isles, keeping them warmer than expected. By contrast, the cold waters of the ACC keep South Georgia cold and heavily glaciated.

So if the waters around Antarctica are cold, and these can have a tremendous impact on the climate of other regions, think about what happens when the Southern Ocean freezes. Large areas of the ocean are below 0 °C (Figures 4.10 and 5.1). However, the ocean does not freeze at 0 °C because water containing dissolved salt has a lower freezing point than fresh water. The temperature at which seawater freezes depends on the concentration of salt, but is usually about −1.8 °C. Large areas around the Antarctic continent have air temperatures below this. Using Figure 4.10 you can estimate how much of the ocean would freeze in a typical winter and stay frozen in the following Antarctic summer.

Satellites can also map the areas of ice on the surface of the ocean, as shown in Figure 5.2. Each coloured dot that makes up the picture represents the mean percentage ice cover over a whole month for an area of about 20 km^2. For example, a value of 50% ice cover means that half of the area (10 km^2) is covered in sea ice, and the other half is open water. As you probably predicted from Figure 4.10, the area of sea ice is much smaller in summer than it is in winter.

■ Why would global warming change the area of sea ice?

☐ As atmospheric temperatures increase over the whole planet, colder air would cover less of the ocean, so the area of sea ice would decrease.

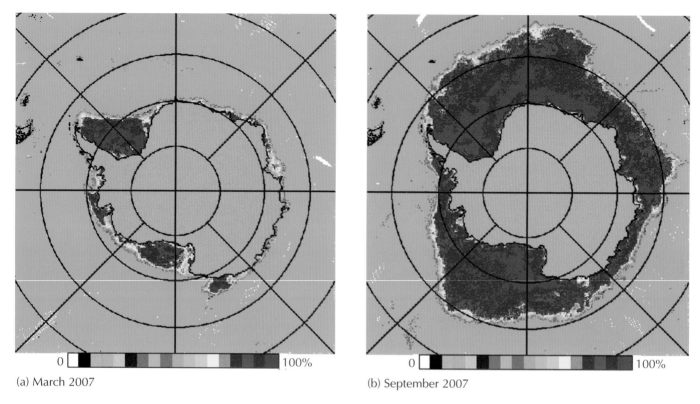

(a) March 2007   (b) September 2007

Figure 5.2   The typical sea ice distribution around Antarctica – light blue represents open water: (a) March 2007 – Antarctic summer; (b) September 2007 – Antarctic winter.

■ Comparing the area of sea surface temperatures lower than −1.8 °C shown in Figure 4.10a with the area of summer sea ice in Figure 5.2a, there is less ice than you would predict. Why would this be the case?

☐ Figure 4.10 shows mean sea surface temperatures over the whole summer, whereas Figure 5.2 shows the amount of sea ice for a single month (February), i.e. in the middle of summer when temperatures are higher than the average for the whole summer.

It is possible to add up the amount of ice represented by each coloured dot in Figure 5.2 to find out the *total* amount of Antarctic sea ice in the Southern Hemisphere over several years (Figure 5.3a) and by taking the mean of each month's data for the whole time series, it is then possible to work out the mean annual cycle of ice area around Antarctica (Figure 5.3b).

You can see that there is the strong annual cycle that you would expect. In winter the area of sea ice is at a maximum, and in the summer it is at a minimum. What is perhaps more surprising is the yearly variability, with more ice in some years and less in others.

■ From Figure 5.3, what is the *minimum* area covered by sea ice during this period, to the nearest million square kilometres?

☐ It is about 2 million km².

■ What is the *maximum* area covered by sea ice during this period to the nearest million square kilometres?

☐ It is about 19 million km².

■ Recall the value given for the area of Antarctica in *The World Factbook* (see Section 4.4.2). How does the maximum area covered by sea ice compare with the land area of Antarctica?

☐ *The World Factbook* states that the area of Antarctica is 14 million km². The graph in Figure 5.3 shows that the area of sea ice can be over 19 million km², so in winter the sea ice area is 5 million km² greater than the total land area of Antarctica!

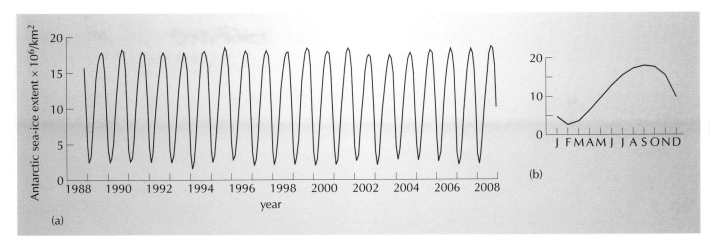

(a)

(b)

Figure 5.3   (a) The area of sea ice in the Southern Ocean from 1988 to 2008. (b) The mean monthly area of sea ice in the Southern Ocean.

The sea ice can cover up to 5 million km² more than the total area of Antarctica. So, in the southern winter, the area of Antarctica effectively more than doubles.

The winter maximum extent of sea ice is absolutely vast, and this huge area of ice is a habitat for Antarctic wildlife such as penguins and seals. But where does the ice come from? Obviously, it is made by seawater freezing. So, if you take a glass of water and mark the level on the side, freeze it and then allow the ice to melt, does the level of water in the glass change? If there were no other processes such as evaporation going on, the level of water would *stay the same* and this is what happens with seawater. So changes in the area of sea ice do not affect sea level. Sea ice is, however, still important for climate because ice is a very good insulator and, once present, it prevents the ocean from further cooling. It also acts like a sponge. In the same way that atmospheric gases are trapped within the snow on the Antarctic continent (see Section 4.7), seawater, and more importantly what is in the seawater, is trapped between ice crystals within the sea ice. Later in this chapter you will see that this trapping of water is critical for sea ice as a habitat.

The fastest way for sea ice to form is through what is called the frazil–pancake cycle. In this cycle, cold temperatures cool the surface of the sea down to the freezing point (−1.8 °C) and ice crystals called **frazil ice** form. Because ice is less dense than water, the crystals float and form a layer on the surface that looks very similar to an oil slick (Figure 5.4a) and is sometimes called 'grease ice'. The ice crystals dampen the higher frequency waves and so within the area covered by the ice, it is calmer. This can be seen in Figure 5.4a – outside the ice slick there are breaking waves, but inside there are not. As it gets calmer the ice crystals stick together to form small plates (Figure 5.4b) that are rounded by constantly bumping into each other – this is called **pancake ice** – and the bumping creates raised edges (Figure 5.4c). As more seawater freezes, more wave energy is dampened and the pancakes grow up to 3 m in diameter. Eventually, the pancakes freeze together and are piled up on top of each other by storms to form larger ice floes. Water freezes onto the bottom and snow falls on the surface of these large floes, increasing their thickness to an average of about 1.5 m. Large areas of this ice are called pack ice (Figure 5.4d). Figure 5.3 shows that the change in ice area from summer to winter is relatively slow. When the sea ice melts and retreats, the process is not the reverse of Figure 5.4. Instead, the ice floes break up into small floes and then decay by melting very rapidly into water.

(a)

(b)

(c)

(d)

Figure 5.4   The frazil–pancake cycle showing the most rapid method of growth of Antarctic sea ice: (a) frazil ice forming a 'slick' on the sea surface; (b) pancake ice; (c) pancake ice with raised edges; (d) pack ice.

5.3   Antarctic habitats

By now you should be aware of the kind of environmental conditions that animals in the Antarctic have to contend with. These characteristics are summarised in Box 5.1. Although we know why Antarctica is cold, why it is ice-covered, and about the variability of the sea ice, none of this explains why there is such a dramatic contrast between the Antarctic land ecosystem and the Antarctic marine ecosystem. The sparse terrestrial ecosystem results from a combination of biogeographical isolation, low and often widely fluctuating temperatures, and drought. By contrast, the marine ecosystem is almost benign.

You should now go to the DVD associated with this book and view the video on the formation and decay of sea ice.

Box 5.1   Antarctic conditions for life

You can think of an ecosystem as a community of animals, microbes and plants plus their physical environment. The conditions of this environment are, of course, fundamental to the life found in it.

Temperature

It takes more heat to raise the temperature of water than it does for air or rock. This means that the temperature of the ocean fluctuates only very slightly – much of the Southern Ocean falls within a 2–4 °C range, just above freezing point (Figure 5.1). However, on land, temperatures can plummet to below −50 °C in winter, whereas a clump of moss on a bare rock could rise to +30 °C on a sunny summer day. So, not only can the land be colder but also it has a much more variable temperature regime.

Water

With about 90% of the planet's non-marine water contained in the Antarctic ice cap, it is not obvious that water availability is a problem for living organisms. However, water is only biologically useful as a liquid. Inland Antarctica is a cold desert, where conditions mimic the freeze-drying process used to preserve foodstuffs. Water availability is of course not a problem in the ocean.

Geography

As the continents drifted apart (Figure 4.14), South America was the last land mass to part company with Antarctica as the Drake Passage opened up some 20 Ma ago (before the present cycle of ice ages and interglacial periods). It then became impossible for large organisms to migrate from warmer climates into Antarctica, and the large animals that remained died out and can be seen as part of the fossil record. The land ice then restricted life to a few limited oases, which made colonisation within the continent difficult. No such physical barriers exist in the ocean.

Suitable habitats are limited on land, and large animals are absent. The terrestrial ecosystem is composed of only two flowering species of simple plants, mosses and lichens, and small invertebrate animals. These organisms are adapted to the incredibly harsh conditions of sub-zero temperatures, a large temperature range, long periods of darkness, and low water availability. In fact, the terrestrial ecosystem is probably similar to what you expected from your knowledge of the Antarctic environment before you began studying this book. Despite these extreme conditions, life can survive in the most unlikely places. For example, one area of continental Antarctica in Southern Victoria Land is known as the 'Dry Valleys', because unusual meteorological conditions have kept them snow- and ice-free for millions of years. The valleys seem totally devoid of life and there are even mummified seals that have accidentally migrated inland from the coast and subsequently been freeze-dried. Yet, among all this sterility, a microbial ecosystem survives by colonising the spaces between crystals in coarse sandstone – this is known as an **endolithic** community (Figure 5.5).

Figure 5.5 Photomicrograph of an endolithic community living within sandstone from the Antarctic Dry Valleys.

The marine ecosystem is very different. Marine wildlife, especially birds and mammals, form one of the major tourist attractions in the region. Even if you are aware that not all areas boast such spectacular 'eco-tourism assets', clearly the Southern Ocean ecosystem is not subject to quite such extreme conditions as the land. But how does this ecosystem compare with others? To take the African bush as an example of another eco-tourism venue with 'charismatic macrofauna', is it possible to describe the two in a way which allows valid comparison? Indeed, what is being compared? Words such as 'rich' and 'diverse' have already been used but these are not easy to quantify – especially when considering such key issues as uncertainty and sustainability.

To introduce ecosystems, the next section compares those of the African bush and the Antarctic marine environment.

5.4   Ecosystems from top to bottom: leopards and leopard seals

Whether in the African savannah or the Southern Ocean, ecosystems share some fundamental similarities. Most fundamental of all to the concept of an ecosystem is the idea that its parts are *connected* by the transfer of carbon and other chemical elements. It all starts with plants or algae, which acquire their carbon from carbon dioxide in the environment. Thereafter, materials are transferred whenever a predator feeds on prey, up the **food chain**, to the **top carnivores**. Each step in the chain is called a **trophic level** and much energy is dissipated with each transfer to a higher level. The top carnivores are often charismatic predators such as leopards in the savannah and leopard seals in the Antarctic, animals that have become icons for their respective regions (Figure 5.6). Because these animals are at the highest trophic level in each ecosystem, a comparison between their biology will tell you a lot about the similarities and differences between the two ecosystems they inhabit.

(a)

(b)

Figure 5.6   (a) A leopard (*Panthera pardus*) in the African savannah. (b) A leopard seal (*Hydrurga leptonyx*) on Antarctic sea ice.

The leopard (Figure 5.6a) is a big cat that inhabits a variety of habitats in Africa and feeds on a range of other mammals – mostly what are considered to be medium-sized **herbivores** such as gazelles. These herbivores in turn feed on large plants, especially the grasses of the surrounding savannah. In ecosystem terminology, the plants are called **primary producers**. The leopard seal (Figure 5.6b) is an equally spectacular Antarctic predator (although it can range as far north as New Zealand). Although slightly bigger than a leopard, leopard seals differ in that they don't normally eat herbivores – their diet is predominantly penguins and other seals, which are themselves **carnivores** – and they are associated with, and breed on, pack ice.

■   Name the trophic levels mentioned so far, starting at the bottom of the food chain.

☐   Primary producers → herbivores → carnivores → top carnivores.

Pictures of the two iconic top carnivores highlight a major distinction between the two habitats: one that is not so much about a difference between tropical and polar, as between land and sea. One thing that leopards do well is climb trees – they can even do this while carrying prey, such as a gazelle. The tree is a large plant that forms part of the baseline trophic level of the ecosystem and provides

117

food for some of the leopard's prey, but it also forms part of the physical fabric of the ecosystem, enabling the leopard to avoid larger predators. Now return to the leopard seal. Where are the plants and where are the equivalent of gazelles? The simple answer is that you would not normally notice them. The marine 'gazelles' are small invertebrate animals similar to prawns. The marine equivalent of the grasses are tiny single-celled algae called **phytoplankton**, which are invisible to the unaided eye.

5.5   The 'grass of the sea'

Carbon enters virtually all food webs through the photosynthetic activity of green plants or algae. These primary producers use sunlight as an energy source to synthesise complex carbon compounds using carbon dioxide and water as raw materials. Animals cannot do this, so they have to eat either plants or other animals. In the open ocean, most plants and algae are microscopic and drift in the upper few tens of metres of the surface waters. These algae (Figure 5.7a) are single-celled and also occur in other aquatic habitats, and even on damp surfaces such as wet walls. The algal cells in the ocean drift with the currents, forming part of the community called the **plankton**. The word 'plankton' comes from the Greek word for 'drifting' and the term **phytoplankton** refers to the algae in the plankton – you will meet zooplankton, their animal counterparts later in this chapter.

Figure 5.7   (a) Photomicrograph of a plankton called *Odontella*, which is made up of several cells. (b) An ocean colour image from the SeaWiFS sensor on the *SeaStar* satellite.

An oak tree weighing hundreds of tonnes and a single phytoplankton cell 25 μm across and weighing half a nanogram (0.000 000 000 5 g) will fulfil exactly the same productive function in their respective ecosystems. They both need light to grow – the oak tree invests much of its **biomass** into a huge trunk so that it can grow above other plants and expose its leaves to as much sunlight as possible (biomass means literally mass of biological material). But the oak tree's strategy simply won't work over most of the ocean. The light needed for plants to grow only penetrates to about 100 m depth in the ocean, and the average ocean depth is approximately 3.8 km. There is no place for a deep-water oak tree and so other plants have evolved to fill the ecological niche.

Individual phytoplankton cells are not visible to the unaided eye but, by collecting samples of water and then filtering out the algae, individual phytoplankton cells can be counted with a microscope. However, this is tedious work, and you could not be certain that one small sample was representative of the water around it. The phytoplankton cells contain the green pigment **chlorophyll**, which enables them to photosynthesise. This pigment also colours the water, and so offers a convenient way of detecting phytoplankton from ships, aircraft or even from space. Some satellites, for example *SeaStar*, are fitted with special sensors that can detect chlorophyll at the ocean surface. An image from the *SeaStar* satellite, collected using the SeaWiFS instrument (Sea-viewing Wide Field-of-view Sensor), is shown in Figure 5.7b. A global dataset can be collected by this instrument every few days.

■ The satellite measures the colour of the ocean. However, what do you notice about the colours on the map in Figure 5.7b?

☐ The colours are not true-to-life. They are false colours used to represent values of chlorophyll concentration, much as colours are used to code for height on some contour maps. Blue represents low chlorophyll concentrations and red very high chlorophyll concentrations.

In contrast to oak trees, the microscopic phytoplankton cells don't need to build complex structures to out-compete other algae. This means that they can grow quite fast – cells can divide as often as once a day. Although this might not seem particularly fast, if you start with a mental picture of a single cell, double it after one day, double each of these the next day, and double all four resulting cells a day later, and so on, you soon get an idea of how quickly the population is growing. This sort of relationship between numbers of cells and time is called an *exponential* increase and, when plotted on a graph, produces a shape like that shown in Figure 5.8. As the population of cells increases, so the rate of production of new cells increases, as they too begin to contribute to the growth. This mathematical relationship, as shown in Figure 5.8, predicts that, if you had one cell on day one, by the end of one month there would be 2^{30} cells! (i.e. two multiplied by itself 30 times). It is certainly true that 2^{30} is a very big number – more than one billion (for a comparison, there are currently about 6 billion people on the planet), and this number is what you would get from just one cell! (Here, a billion means a thousand million, or 10^9.) Given that a litre of seawater typically contains a million (10^6) algal cells, there seems to be enormous potential to generate huge amounts of phytoplankton in a very short time. *In theory*, if left for only for a few months, this type of exponential increase in phytoplankton could produce a weight equal to that of the Earth!

Although in theory phytoplankton can grow this fast, in practice they obviously do not, otherwise the oceans would, long ago, have become completely smothered. The factors that prevent this exponential growth include a

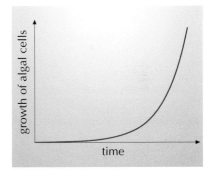

Figure 5.8 Exponential growth of algal cells.

requirement for a constant supply of sunlight, carbon dioxide, water and minerals such as nitrogen, phosphorus and iron for continued growth. Minerals are in scarce supply in some parts of the ocean. In addition, the phytoplankton are eaten by herbivores.

■ Is there a region in Figure 5.7b where the minerals essential for growth could be in short supply in the oceans?

☐ The areas that are dark blue, since they represent a low concentration of chlorophyll.

Figure 5.7b shows that oceanic vegetation is not evenly distributed. The regions that are colour-coded red and orange signify a high abundance of phytoplankton and you could suggest that these areas are places where conditions are suitable for phytoplankton growth, perhaps because of a good supply of the extra mineral salts that the algae need. The areas colour-coded blue and purple have low abundance, and growth conditions are less favourable.

Phytoplankton cells die for a number of reasons, including viral infection and failure to get enough light to survive. A diverse range of grazing animals (herbivores) feed on both living and dead phytoplankton cells. The herbivores of the ocean are very efficient, and they keep the phytoplankton population at a steady level. In the Antarctic marine ecosystem, one of the most important grazers is a shrimp-like animal commonly known as 'krill'.

5.6   Krill – an 'invisible' herbivore

Figure 5.9 Antarctic krill (*Euphausia superba*) – the 'invisible' herbivore. Average body length 5 cm.

The previous section noted that the marine ecosystem does not have conspicuous herbivores. This does not mean that they don't exist. Krill are one of the most important consumers of phytoplankton in many parts of the ocean around Antarctica. There are several species but the most common is *Euphausia superba*, which grows up to 5–6 cm long when adult (Figure 5.9). Although a lot smaller than a gazelle, or any other mammal, krill are quite large by marine herbivore standards, where most of the grazing animals range in size from fractions of a millimetre up to a few millimetres. They tend to be carried along by currents and turbulence in the oceans and, together with their single-celled algal food source, form part of the plankton. Animal plankton are collectively known as **zooplankton**, but not all of them are herbivorous – even krill can graze successfully on other small zooplankton.

As a biological 'rule of thumb', small animals are energetic, fast growing and short-lived, while big ones tend to be a bit slower but live longer – for a comparison think of a small scurrying mouse and a huge lumbering elephant. The small herbivores in the oceans would be expected to feed and grow rapidly. This means that they can respond very quickly to an increase in phytoplankton, and so the phytoplankton and grazer populations go through very similar cycles as the amount of phytoplankton changes. As the numbers of phytoplankton increase, the grazers multiply in the face of a food 'surplus', and so are very effective in controlling the abundance of phytoplankton.

A krill is quite a large zooplankton, and it is substantially larger than the phytoplankton on which it feeds. For example, if you magnified both organisms 1000-fold, an average alga would be about the size of a squash ball, while the krill would be the length of four buses. Not surprisingly, krill are abundant in the parts of the Southern Ocean with a dense food supply – that is, of course, large numbers of phytoplankton. Cynthia Tynan (1998) investigated the relationship between these large-scale patterns of distribution of the different trophic levels in the Southern Ocean (Figure 5.10). Figure 5.10a is an ocean colour map of phytoplankton production in the Southern Ocean derived from data collected over a period of about a year in the 1990s, and so is an average. Figure 5.10b is a distribution map of catches of krill, based largely on data collected using large nets and over several years from a pioneering study of the Antarctic marine ecosystem in the 1930s called the Discovery Investigations. (You will learn more about this study in Chapter 6.)

(a)   (b)

Figure 5.10   (a) An ocean colour image of the Antarctic in the 1990s; the white line marks the position of a minor ocean front. (b) The distribution of krill caught by nets in the 1930s; the blue line represents the position of the polar front.

The two maps certainly show that there is a similarity between the distribution of krill and its main food supply. However, these data sets should be treated with caution. Before drawing any firm conclusions, the data sets must be comparable.

■   What features of the data might reduce the reliability of the comparison?

☐   There are uncertainties associated with each map. The process of averaging data over long periods of time introduces uncertainty, especially where spatial coverage is poor and uneven. There is also uncertainty in comparing two data sets that are collected by very different techniques and subjected to different averaging processes. Perhaps most importantly, the two sets of data were collected more than 50 years apart.

The analysis of ecosystem data interweaves environmental and biological variability – called patchiness – in both space and time. In addition, there is an uncertainty in all of the quantities measured. It is difficult to understand completely an ecosystem.

The distribution of krill is not just patchy on the very large scales covered by Figure 5.10b. Krill are zooplankton and are carried along in the Antarctic Circumpolar Current. However, they can also swim strongly enough to control their position relative to each other over distances of up to tens of metres. In the same way that wildebeest form herds on the African savannah, krill are commonly found in large groups called 'swarms' that can range from tens of metres to a kilometre or more across, and they can move coherently like fish schools. Inside a swarm, there may be more than a thousand animals per cubic metre of seawater, although they are not permanent groups and they can disperse and re-form on timescales from hours to days. The swarms can even change in size and shape from day to night, with krill forming swarms near the surface at night and dispersing at depth during the day. Armed with this knowledge about the behaviour of krill, you can immediately see why comparing data such as that in Figure 5.10 is a problem. To find out more about the marine ecosystem, we need to know how much krill is living there – in other words, we need a value for krill biomass.

■ Can you see any potential problems with deriving krill biomass by using nets to catch krill?

☐ The problem is how to get an accurate value for the krill numbers – and hence biomass. Because of the patchy distribution, if only a few samples are taken, you could go through the middle of a krill swarm, or even miss it altogether. This would greatly affect your overall answer for the biomass.

Until recently, nearly all sampling of life in the oceans involved catching organisms with various nets and other sampling devices. This method has been compared to using a helicopter above the clouds to sample life on land – you cannot see what you are fishing for, or how representative it is of the local ecosystem. To increase confidence in our data on krill we could take more measurements. If, for example, you took thousands of net samples, you might be confident that you have sampled a larger proportion of the total krill population, and so smoothed out the natural variability (or patchiness) in the system. Today, echo sounders in ships are used routinely to measure the amount of krill in the water as a ship moves along (Figure 5.11). This method gives a very high resolution picture of the krill abundance – but, of course, only beneath the ship. So, it still does not come close to the spatial coverage of satellite data, such as that shown in Figure 5.10a.

distance

sea surface

depth

sea floor

Figure 5.11   An echo-sounder trace showing a krill swarm. The ship moves from left to right and the colours represent the amount of krill in the water column. The red–brown patch in the centre is a krill swarm.

If this swarming behaviour is a nightmare for biologists trying to quantify krill in the ecosystem, it is a heaven-sent opportunity for many of the animals that feed on krill, and the next section looks at one such animal – the blue whale.

5.7   The blue whale – a marine anteater?

Blue whales are probably the largest animals ever to have lived on the planet. Adults can be over 30 m long and weigh more than 100 tonnes. Paradoxically, they feed by filtering very small animals – zooplankton (such as krill) and fish – out of the water by taking a huge mouthful of water (Figure 5.12), and then straining out the animals through long fibrous plates called baleen, which hang down from the roof of their mouth. For a large blue whale, 'huge mouthful' means about 70 cubic metres of seawater – which is more than half of the weight of the whale itself (a cubic metre of seawater weighs just over 1 tonne).

Figure 5.12   A blue whale (*Balaenoptera musculus*).

Just as there is a large contrast between the size of krill and phytoplankton, there is an equally impressive difference in size between whales and krill. Returning to the earlier size comparison, where organism sizes were increased 1000-fold, krill are the size of four buses (about 50 m), whereas the length of a blue whale would be about 30 km! This predator–prey size ratio is about the same as that between anteaters and ants. But even with the capacity to filter up to 70 tonnes of water in one go, blue whales could not feed on krill if they didn't occur in swarms. Biologists have estimated that a blue whale needs about 3 tonnes of krill per day to survive – this is about 3 million krill, at a gram each. Imagine how much effort this would take if krill occurred in ones and twos. Blue whales – and several other large predators – can only exploit krill as their main food supply *because* swarming makes krill easy to catch in large numbers.

5.8   Production and biomass – putting some numbers into the ecosystem

To understand how this particular ecosystem functions, and perhaps to compare it with others, we need to follow the fate of phytoplankton material through the food web. As well as looking at biomass, we must consider its increase (that is, production) and the efficiency of *transfer* between the trophic levels – the transfer is the ratio between the amount of food eaten and the amount of production.

Blue whales need about 3 tonnes of krill per day to live. In an area with a very good food supply, krill can grow by 2–3% of their body mass per day; their growth rate slows as they approach their maximum size. For the whale's feeding to be sustained by krill production, it needs to forage over an area of the ocean which will yield 3 tonnes of krill per day.

■   Assuming a mean krill growth rate of 2.5% of body mass per day, what biomass of krill is required to sustain one blue whale?

☐   Assuming a growth rate of 2.5% body mass per day:

1 tonne of krill produces 2.5 ÷ 100 = 0.025 tonnes of extra krill per day.

To obtain 3 tonnes of *extra* krill body mass per day requires:

3 ÷ 0.025 = 120 tonnes of krill.

This biomass of krill will typically occupy an area between 5 and 40 km^2 (depending on the local population density and number of swarms).

■   Assuming that a 100-tonne blue whale eats 3 tonnes of krill per day, how long will it take for the whale to consume the equivalent of its own body mass?

☐   This will take:

100 ÷ 3 = 33.3 days, i.e. just over a month.

The krill will, in turn, need to eat more than 3 tonnes of phytoplankton to produce this amount of growth. In fact, the krill need about 25 tonnes of phytoplankton to produce 3 tonnes of biomass. By now you will be asking, what would be the mass of phytoplankton required for 25 tonnes of phytoplankton production, so that the system remains in balance?

■ Given that typical daily phytoplankton production is about 20% of biomass, how much phytoplankton will be required to produce 25 tonnes per day?

☐ One tonne of phytoplankton produces:

$20 \div 100 = 0.2$ tonnes of extra phytoplankton per day at a growth rate of 20%.

To get 25 tonnes of extra phytoplankton in the study area requires:

$25 \div 0.2 = 125$ tonnes.

We now have 'numbers' for the three trophic levels. In 5–40 km^2 of ocean, there is almost the same biomass of whale (100 tonnes), krill (120 tonnes) and phytoplankton (125 tonnes). The key to the food chain is the very different productivities at the three trophic levels. Phytoplankton grow fast – the daily production in the study area is 25 tonnes, or 20% growth. The production of krill in the same area was 3 tonnes at 2.5% growth. The whale would probably gain only 50–100 kg of body mass per day – a growth rate of 0.0005–0.001%. Looking at trophic levels in terms of *productivity* rather than biomass (productivity is simply the rate of production), the pattern is clear: the system is remarkably inefficient at turning phytoplankton into whale biomass.

■ If the whale really does eat 3 tonnes of food per day, but only builds up 50–100 kg of body mass, what happens to the rest of the food?

☐ Some of the food that the whale eats, such as the exoskeleton of the krill, is indigestible, so it is excreted as faeces.

Most of the food that passes through the gut wall of the whale is assimilated – but is then used as fuel to run the whale's muscles and other tissues, and provide the heat to maintain its constant body temperature.

Not much of the energy from primary producers appears in higher trophic levels, and birds and mammals are especially 'uneconomical' to run – typically accumulating only 2–4% of their food intake as production (compared with a figure of about 10% for cold-blooded vertebrates such as fish).

Turning 25 tonnes of phytoplankton into 0.1 tonne of whale blubber doesn't look all that impressive as a demonstration of efficiency. Nearly all the phytoplankton biomass has been used by the krill and whale to produce energy, or excreted as faeces. Other, more complex food webs can be even less efficient. The 'alga-to-krill-to-whale' food chain involves only two transfers. Consider a leopard seal eating a young Weddell seal which, in turn, fed on fish which ate krill.

■ How many trophic levels are involved in this food chain?

☐ There are five trophic levels – three predators (leopard seal, Weddell seal and fish), a herbivore (krill) and primary producers (phytoplankton).

This food web is more complex with an additional two trophic levels, and here only about 0.002% of phytoplankton biomass will be converted into new leopard seal biomass. Figure 5.13 shows a simple representation of the Southern Ocean food web, and you can see that food chains are typically quite short, involving few trophic levels. It is also obvious that most of the arrows eventually reach or start from the krill. Where a single species plays a key role in an ecosystem, it is often termed a **keystone species**.

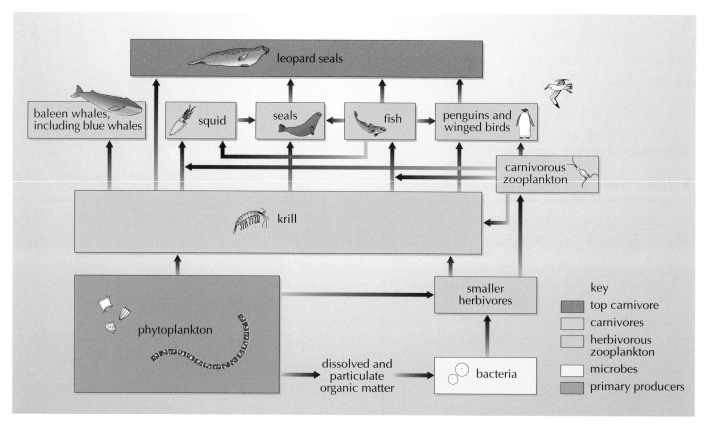

Figure 5.13   Highly simplified schematic diagram of the Antarctic open-ocean ecosystem, illustrating the importance of krill. Note that waste products from all the animals add dissolved and particulate organic matter to the water, which feed on bacteria. Animals and microbes occurring in the sediment are not shown.

You can see from Figure 5.13 that the phytoplankton → krill → whale food chain is one of the simplest in the Antarctic. This comparatively efficient route for turning plant growth into mammal tissue involves a large, long-lived animal. The more complex trophic structures sustain a smaller biomass of top predators simply because there are greater energy losses as a result of the larger number of intermediate trophic levels.

Figure 5.7b shows that the phytoplankton growth that sustains the ecosystem is typically quite low in the Southern Ocean. You can use this fairly moderate level of production to run 'expensive' predators such as whales *only* if you have a trophic structure that channels phytoplankton production efficiently to the top predators.

■   What sort of food chains are most efficient at channelling the phytoplankton production efficiently to the top predators?

☐   Food chains with few trophic levels.

These short food chains are a dominant feature of the Southern Ocean (Figure 5.13) and work because of patchiness (Figure 5.11) – the krill feed on local phytoplankton hot spots and whales can only survive by feeding on krill because they occur in swarms. The Antarctic marine ecosystem is clearly not all that productive; neither is it particularly diverse, despite the conspicuous predators such as whales, seals and penguins.

5.9   The ice–ocean ecosystem

So far, this chapter has considered an open-ocean ecosystem. In Section 5.2 you saw that the Southern Ocean is covered by up to 19×10^6 km^2 of sea ice at certain times of the year. What effect does this have on the ecosystem? Again considering the simple phytoplankton $\rightarrow$ krill $\rightarrow$ whale food chain, how are these three organisms affected by sea ice? For the phytoplankton, the most important effect is loss of light. Sea ice is not clear like freshwater ice, and snow lying on the ice blocks out even more light.

■   How would the decrease in light affect phytoplankton production?

☐   The phytoplankton need light to photosynthesise so there would be a dramatic decrease in production.

At the other end of this particular food chain, sea ice poses a major problem for whales and other air-breathing animals. If they cannot get to the surface, they cannot breathe. A dense cover of sea ice means the affected parts of the ocean are off-limits for whales, so some species (such as the blue whale) migrate north to the tropics for the southern winter. On the other hand, krill are not affected directly by sea ice. In fact, the nooks and crannies underneath older sea ice provide a shelter where krill can hide from fish and other predators. But what are the krill eating?

Figure 5.4a shows how the slurry of ice crystals traps anything suspended in the water – including phytoplankton. As the ice grows, there are many cavities and channels between the crystals that are rich in the chemicals needed for phytoplankton growth. Despite low temperatures and low light, some algal cells continue to grow within the sea ice. Often the density of algae is so high that it can colour this sea ice, although these algal cells contain brown pigment that masks the green colour of the chlorophyll, so the ice appears brown (Figure 5.14). So, krill also have a food supply in winter – they can graze on the algae trapped in the ice, and on the bottom of the sea ice.

Figure 5.14   Antarctic pack ice showing green–brown algae trapped in the sea-ice crystal matrix.

127

Far from being a hostile habitat, the sea ice provides both food and shelter for krill. Other predators can also take advantage of the ice. The crabeater seal spends its whole life cycle on the Antarctic pack ice (Figure 5.15) and, despite its name, lives on krill. Although you may not have heard of this species, it is the world's most abundant seal, with an estimated population of 12 million living in Antarctica.

Figure 5.15   Crabeater seals (*Lobodon carcinophagus*) basking on the Antarctic pack ice.

5.10   Planet engineering with plankton

Concern over the human impact on the global climate has led to a huge surge of interest in the mechanisms by which the biosphere influences the composition of the atmosphere. In Book 3, you will see that the concentration of carbon dioxide in the atmosphere is increasing, but this increase is just a by-product of a complex 'carbon cycle' that moves carbon around the planet. The IPCC states that there are approximately 2000×10^9 tonnes of carbon stored on land, and approximately 730×10^9 tonnes stored in the atmosphere. In comparison, there is approximately $38\,000 \times 10^9$ tonnes of carbon stored in the oceans. Carbon dioxide is taken up by plants, including oceanic phytoplankton, which constitutes a carbon 'sink', helping to reduce the so-called 'greenhouse effect'. However, other processes in the biosphere return some of this carbon to the atmosphere. To predict the impact of future climate changes, we need an understanding of the balance between these biological 'sources' and 'sinks'.

Carbon dioxide is not thought to be a limiting resource for ocean phytoplankton. The limiting factors include elements such as nitrogen, phosphorus, silicon and sulfur that the phytoplankton require to build biomass. All of these nutrients are dissolved in seawater and removed by phytoplankton growth. Figure 5.7b shows that global plankton production (shown as ocean colour) does not occur uniformly but, interestingly, the oceans in some areas have high nutrient levels but low chlorophyll values. If there are high nutrient levels, what else is missing to prevent the phytoplankton growing? Some of the controls were identified earlier in this chapter: lack of light, removal of phytoplankton by grazing, and so on. There is now strong evidence that trace elements such as iron play a crucial role in algal growth. Iron is the most abundant element on the planet as a whole, but is only present in trace amounts in seawater. Experiments in laboratories and in the field have shown that the addition of dissolved iron to the environment of Southern Ocean phytoplankton allows them to grow faster and to use up more of the available supply of other nutrients.

This raises an intriguing possibility. Would it be possible to 'seed' the Southern Ocean with iron and engineer a massive phytoplankton bloom? If this happened, would it remove some, or even all, of the extra carbon dioxide which human activity has introduced to the atmosphere over the last century? John Martin, one of the scientists who originated the 'iron fertilisation hypothesis', said 'You give me half a tanker of iron, and I'll give you the next ice age' (cited in Kunzig, 1999).

Before you take this comment at face value, you should stop to think about some of what you have learned in this book. Would it be a feasible project? If it was, and phytoplankton production in the Southern Ocean increased to levels where it reduced the amount of carbon in the atmosphere, would all of this carbon be removed on a long-term basis? Would there be other implications for the marine ecosystem, and how would you go about assessing the various impacts that planetary engineering on this scale could involve? Finally, what legal and political framework exists to regulate such actions? These sorts of ideas are types of *mitigation* and you will learn more about them in Book 3.

5.11   Conclusions

The Southern Ocean and the sea ice are key components of the Antarctic ecosystem. Terrestrial life is as sparse as you would expect. In contrast, the ocean has an ecosystem with several conspicuous animal groups, which suggests that the region is biologically productive. However, large animals like whales can only survive if the food web is simple and consists of few trophic levels. Finally, the marine ecosystem may have the potential to reduce global warming.

5.12   Summary of Chapter 5

5.1 The Antarctic Circumpolar Current regulates and extends the Antarctic environment as far north as the polar front. The waters south of the polar front circulate clockwise around Antarctica.

5.2 The sea surface freezes at −1.8 °C, and sea ice covers an area greater than the size of Antarctica in winter but less than a quarter of this area at the height of summer. The frazil–pancake cycle is the most rapid means of forming pack ice and seawater is trapped between the ice crystals.

5.3 Food webs consist of primary producers, herbivores, carnivores and top carnivores and these are structured into trophic levels.

5.4 The transfer of energy between trophic levels is very inefficient.

5.5 Plants and animals are not distributed uniformly across the Southern Ocean (or any other ocean), and physical factors such as ocean circulation play a major role in ecosystem variability.

5.6 Krill are the key Antarctic species and large predators can be supported as a result of their swarming behaviour.

5.7 The sea ice around Antarctica is a component of the krill habitat.

5.8 Antarctic productivity may be limited by a lack of iron.

Questions for Chapter 5

Question 5.1

In a few sentences describe and compare the climate of two islands, one on either side of the polar front.

Question 5.2

Assign the following animals to one of the trophic levels in the marine ecosystem: (a) killer whale; (b) penguin; (c) krill; (d) baleen whale; (e) phytoplankton; (f) crabeater seal.

Now draw a simplified food web with five boxes to show the links between the trophic levels. Finally, where would humans appear in this food web?

Question 5.3

At which stage of sea-ice growth do the primary producers become entrained in the ice, and at which time of the year would you expect this to happen?

Question 5.4

In about 50 words, describe why you would not expect all sea ice to contain a brown layer of chlorophyll.

Question 5.5

When sea ice decays and retreats, what is the effect on sea level?

Question 5.6

Why are animals such as the blue whale able to survive on krill?

Question 5.7

Why could the addition of iron to the Southern Ocean mitigate climate change?

References

Kunzig, R. (1999) *The Restless Sea*, New York, W.W. Norton and Company.

Tynan, C.T. (1998) 'Ecological importance of the southern boundary of the Antarctic circumpolar current', *Nature*, vol. 392, pp. 708–10.

Chapter 6
From exploitation to the endgame: Antarctic governance

6.1   Introduction

Previous chapters discussed what happened once the pressures of globalisation reached Antarctica in the 19th century. They noted the unregulated exploitation of its resources and the collapse of whole populations of marine mammals, together with the wider ecological repercussions of such decimation. It was concluded that exploitation is only sustainable when it does not destroy the structure of the ecosystem which produces the harvest. This chapter explores how governance of the resources in Antarctica has evolved to cope with exploitation.

Antarctica is a good region for this investigation because interventions have been generally well recorded as a result of the late arrival of humans on the scene. It provides a special case in the development of international governance, but it also deserves special attention because of the potential effect that events in Antarctica could have on the rest of the world as the climate warms up.

Politics and Antarctica had a quiet introduction. In 1908 the British Government made a claim for the Antarctic Peninsula from 20° W to 80° W, based on the discoveries of previous British explorers (Table 4.1). Initially, this claim seemed to go unnoticed on the international scene – but this was a time of great political upheaval in the western world and Antarctica was a long way away. However, it did not take long for other nations to become interested in the continent and its potential riches.

6.2   Exploitation continues

While expeditions continued to explore Antarctica (see Table 4.1), sealing continued until fur seal (*Arctocephalus* sp.) and elephant seal (*Mirounga leonina*) populations diminished to the point where it was no longer commercially profitable to send ships to South Georgia. At first sight, human predation on seals was following a predator–prey cycle but, because predator numbers did not decrease as prey numbers fell, there was a massive population crash and seal numbers fell to such low levels that it was thought they may never recover. (Indeed, in 1958 a South Georgia survey showed that there were still fewer than 100 pairs of fur seals left. Their numbers have now risen to very high levels as you will discover later in this chapter.) However, there were other marine resources to exploit – the whales.

Returning to the voyages listed in Table 4.1, the Swedish South Polar Expedition led by Otto Nordenskjöld (1869–1928) is one of particular note. The captain of Nordenskjöld's ship *Antarctic* was the Norwegian Carl Larsen (1860–1924) and the expedition had a 'colourful' history. The ship was wrecked, and the expedition members and crew were rescued from the Antarctic Peninsula by the

Argentinian Navy (the ship they used, *Uruguay*, can still be seen in Buenos Aires). At the banquet to celebrate this rescue, Larsen said:

> I tank youse very mooch and dees is all vary nice and youse vary kind to mes, bot I ask youse ven I am here vy don't youse take dese vales at your doors, dems vary big vales and I seen dem in houndreds and tousands.

(originally transcribed in 1903, quoted in Headland, 1984)

In the early 1900s, whales were used for a wide variety of purposes including food, lighting oil, and the manufacture of many products from soap to umbrellas to explosives. Larsen was a shrewd businessman and he knew that the output of northern European whaling stations was falling thus creating a gap in the market. With this in mind, he set up the Compañia Argentina de Pesca, with himself as whaling manager, and returned to Norway to fit out a whaling expedition. In 1904 he set off to South Georgia, an Antarctic region that he knew was particularly abundant in whales.

■ Which country claimed ownership of South Georgia?

☐ Captain James Cook made the first landing and he claimed the island for Britain in January 1775.

Larsen set up a whaling station at a place he called Grytviken on South Georgia (Figure 6.1). ('Grytviken' is Norwegian for 'pot cove' – the pots being those left by the sealers for boiling blubber.) His company paid a fee to the British government for using the island *and* for the whales they caught. The whaling fleet consisted of small, fast 'catcher' boats that harpooned whales and towed the carcasses to Grytviken for processing. In their first year the catcher boats barely had to leave the harbour to take humpback whales (*Megaptera novaeangliae*)

Figure 6.1   Grytviken whaling station in the early 20th century. There is a blue whale on the flensing plan (the place where the blubber is stripped from the carcass). On the middle left-hand side of the picture there are some pigs (feeding on blubber) which were introduced to South Georgia.

and the slaughter began. That year, Larsen took 235 whales made up of 189 humpbacks, 22 fin whales (*Balaenoptera physalus*), 17 blue whales (*Balaenoptera musculus*) and 7 right whales (*Eubalaena australis*). These whales provided a total of about 1250 tons of oil although, because of over-supply, the price of oil crashed to its lowest level ever (Jackson, 1978). This crash affected profits, but Larsen persevered and the price of oil soon rose, making the operation very profitable. With booming profits, whaling became an international industry in this region and, within 10 years, there were 10 operational shore-based whaling stations (Figure 6.1).

Setting up a whaling station in Antarctica was extremely expensive but, as the historian Gordon Jackson (1978) pointed out, there was a 'marriage of British resources and Norwegian labour … that was the nature of "British" whaling for the rest of its life'. Norwegian was the language spoken at virtually all of the stations. But the situation took a strange twist when the first completely British whaling company – Salvesen's New Whaling Company – was prevented from setting up a station on South Georgia by the British Colonial Office, which was trying to control the whaling. Jackson noted 'the incongruity of a British territory admitting foreigners and excluding Britons'. Eventually, the British government relented and Salvesen set up Leith whaling station in 1909. The impact of the rapidly developing industry and the vast catches were predictable, even without a complex understanding of the Antarctic marine ecosystem. An old northern whaler told one of the southern whalers in 1912:

> that they had better make hay while the sun shone, as if seven whalers were getting 7000 whales in one spot, it would not be very long before the southern whale fishery would follow the northern whale fishery, and the whales would practically disappear from the sea.

> (quoted in Jackson, 1978)

The real leap in technology that enabled whaling to continue when 'one spot' was fished out came with the introduction of the first factory ships in 1925. These ships allowed the industry to exploit whales at sea, where it was beyond the control of the British government.

■ What is an obvious advantage in using factory ships?

☐ The factory ships allowed the small catcher boats to cover a much wider geographical area, and enabled the hunters to track the whales closely.

Huge factory ships operated all along the Antarctic Peninsula and they moored in sheltered coves to process the whales that were caught. However, the impact of the whalers was not solely on the marine ecosystem.

■ What effect did the whalers have on the land-based ecosystem?

☐ They introduced non-native species.

The whalers deliberately introduced reindeer, cattle and pigs (you can see the latter feeding on whale blubber in Figure 6.1) to provide a varied diet. Earlier in this book, you saw that island ecosystems are vulnerable, and the introduction of a new species such as reindeer that could easily survive in the environment was immediate and significant. (There are still several hundred reindeer on the island

(Figure 6.2), and discussions continue as to whether to remove them or not.) The whalers also accidentally introduced rats and mice. As on Lord Howe Island (Section 2.7), the rats have devastated the local bird life. In fact, the geographical expansion of both the rat and reindeer populations across South Georgia has been limited only by their inability to cross the glaciers that cover the island.

Figure 6.2   Reindeer (*Rangifer tarandus*) at a derelict whaling station on South Georgia.

So, Britain controlled much of the whaling in the Southern Ocean in the first half of the 20th century when the industry was based on South Georgia. But the people who worked at the whaling stations were British, Norwegian, Chilean and Argentinian. As the numbers of large whales began to drop, the industry shifted its targeted species to smaller animals. However, as catches fell, so did the revenue received by the British government. The British Colonial Office was well aware of what was happening and, in a bid to prevent the total collapse of whale stocks, it set up the first long-term Antarctic research programme. The programme was called The Discovery Investigations, named after the ship it was given (Captain Scott's ship from his expedition in 1901).

6.3   Understanding the impacts of unsustainable development: The Discovery Investigations

Now is a good time to do the website activity associated with this part of the chapter.

In 1911 the government formed a committee to make recommendations about a sustainable whaling industry to prevent a 'boom and bust'. After a delay caused by World War I, the committee came up with 36 recommendations, some of which are particularly interesting in the light of current environmental perspectives. The key recommendations included:

(2) The food for whales, whether consisting of plankton or fish, should be carefully investigated.

(6) An experienced zoologist should be deputed to work for some time at one or more of the whaling stations.

(11) The utmost economy must be observed in the utilization of all whale products, and every effort should be made to prevent the catching of more whales than can be commercially utilized.

(22) Study of the life history and habits of the seals of the Dependencies [the name the British gave to the Antarctic] should form part of the work of the biologists attached to the proposed expedition.

(27) A complete hydrographical survey of the Dependencies is necessary both in the general interest of navigation and in the local interests of the whaling industry.

(35) Expenses incurred in connection with the economic development of the Dependencies and in particular with the preservation of the whaling industry may properly form charge against revenue raised in the Dependencies and additional taxation may rightly be imposed upon the whaling and sealing industries for the purpose of meeting such expenditure.

(Colonial Office, UK, 1920)

Even from today's viewpoint, these are forward-thinking recommendations. However, the ideas behind this list are not so different from Weddell's views about protecting seal populations in 1825 (see Chapter 4) – so again the 'green perspective' is neither new nor original. The committee must have realised that it could not stop whaling but that understanding how to harvest the whales sustainably would allow the revenues to continue. You can get an idea of the sums involved if the costs are converted into current real terms (early 21st century). On this basis, the cost of the Discovery Investigations programme was almost £18.5 million up to 1932. From recommendation (35), it is evident that this was only a fraction of the revenue from South Georgia.

The Discovery Investigations began in 1925 and early results showed that the number of whales caught in just one month in 1926 from South Georgia was huge (Figure 6.3). A painting by Alister Hardy (a member of the

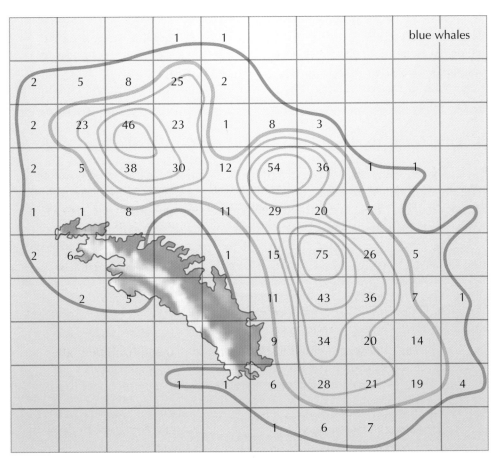

Figure 6.3 The distribution of blue whales caught around South Georgia in December 1926. The number in each box represents the number of animals caught. Contours are drawn at intervals of 10 animals.

Figure 6.4   Painting by Alister Hardy (1896–1985) of a whale carcass awaiting flensing at Grytviken (Hardy, 1967).

Discovery Investigations team) conveys the industrial scale of the South Georgia whaling (Figure 6.4) in a more honest way than Figure 6.1. The investigations transformed our knowledge of whale biology as scientists could study recently caught carcasses. For example, they were able to measure the size and gestation period for different species, how often they conceived, and so on. The investigations also gave the first demonstration of the importance of krill in the Antarctic marine ecosystem. However, there were notable omissions from the findings, the most obvious being a reliable estimate of whale numbers.

The investigations ended their fieldwork in the late 1940s although they continued to publish scientific work until the 1970s. Today, we can see that the hunters jumped species too quickly for the scientists to understand what was happening and the whaling industry collapsed through overhunting. Without this understanding there was virtually no hope of regulating the system.

From one perspective you could argue that the investigations programme was a costly failure. However, it taught us a lot about the Antarctic marine environment. It was the first to identify the continuous nature of the polar front around Antarctica; it discovered the life cycle of krill and linked their distribution to the distribution of whales (Figure 5.7); it also studied ocean circulation in these regions. What it could *not* do as a national scientific expedition was to establish an international policy to prevent the whale slaughter.

At the end of World War II, there were an estimated 50 000 blue whales in the Antarctic. By 1970, American scientists estimated that probably no more than 500 remained. One of the authors of this book worked on research ships in the South Georgia region for almost 10 years and, in that time, never saw a blue whale. Even with the benefits of modern technology, we cannot yet say with certainty where blue whales migrate to, what their full life history is, or even if they will ever recover to their former numbers – and this is despite their being the largest animals *ever* to have lived on Earth.

6.4   The International Whaling Commission

During the 'hunting frenzy' of the early 20th century, even some of the whalers thought there should be some form of international management of the whaling industry and the League of Nations set up a Whaling Committee. By 1946 this had become the International Whaling Commission (IWC) and its terms of reference were given by a treaty known as the International Convention for the Regulation of Whaling. Its aims were similar to those of the Discovery Investigations but this time the organisation was a real international agency. The treaty stated that the IWC should be responsible for 'the orderly development of the whaling industry', and initially the commission set quotas based on estimates of the stocks of whales. Unfortunately, these quotas were based on pre-war population estimates, and in addition, despite setting a quota, the IWC did not assess the claims of individual nations to the whale stocks. Some countries (e.g. the USA) believed that 'freedom of the seas' was important, and that whaling could be managed by setting an overall catch quota. Factory ships would then sail wherever they wanted, report weekly catches and, when the quota was reached, all whaling would be stopped.

■ What was the flaw in this strategy?

☐ The whalers would have to be honest and not lie about the numbers of whales caught.

All whaling countries continually and demonstrably lied about catches and, of course, whale numbers decreased. As a result, the whaling nations found it increasingly difficult to make 'adequate' profits. In 1965 two eminent scientists wrote:

> The major Antarctic stocks of blue and fin whales could, if properly managed, produce annually, and in perpetuity, a total of 25 000 whales. However, they have been reduced far below the level which would provide these maximum sustainable yields and at present any catches in excess of about 4000 fin whales and a few blue whales would deplete the stocks. Despite this knowledge, in the 1964–65 season 14 000 fin whales were killed. … Never was a case for international action so obvious, and perhaps the response been so inadequate.

> (Lucas and Cole, 1965)

Despite such strong language, it was not until 1982 that the IWC agreed to a moratorium on *all* whale stocks, to begin in 1985–6. This moratorium remains in force at the beginning of the 21st century. Although there were violent and global anti-whaling protests at this time, it was only commercial reasons that stopped whaling. There was simply not enough profit left. The IWC remains convinced that the populations of whales will recover now that commercial hunting has ceased, and when this happens, according to the Convention, whaling should resume.

■ Would you expect the whale numbers to recover to their pre-hunting levels?

☐ No because different species have different rates of reproduction and will recover at different rates.

Minke whales (*Balaenoptera acutorostrata*) seem to be recovering very rapidly and, at the start of the 21st century, the global population was estimated to be about 1 million animals. Other species have not recovered so well, and blue whale stocks do not appear to be recovering at all. However, if whaling resumed on a 'recovered' species then environmental groups would probably find other reasons to protest against whaling. The politics of whaling are now governed less by scientific arguments about numbers of animals and reproduction rates than by the ethics of killing whales.

■ In view of the different rates of reproduction of whale species, how should a return to whaling be managed?

☐ Different species should be declared 'available' to hunt *only* when they have exceeded their own targeted population levels. Further, there should be different quotas set for each individual species based on estimates of sustainable hunting. Of course, this depends on whalers being honest and not exceeding quotas.

The argument is complicated by the fact that, although commercial whaling ceased in 1985, 'scientific whaling' – that is whaling conducted for the purposes of studying the animals – has never stopped. Japan takes approximately 400 minke whales per year to study the average age of the animals and reproductive rates. Using this data they can estimate animal numbers, and then work out how many whales could be sustainably harvested. The whale meat is also sold, but this contributes to the cost of the research.

6.4.1 The end of Antarctic whaling

As whales became commercially extinct, the whaling stations on South Georgia closed one by one. Eventually, even the largest and most efficient whaling station at Grytviken was closed in 1964. The whaling companies thought they would be able to resume whaling at a future date and so the stations were 'mothballed', the companies leaving behind large amounts of the debris including whalebones, scrap metal, barrels and even ships (Figure 6.5).

(a)

(b)

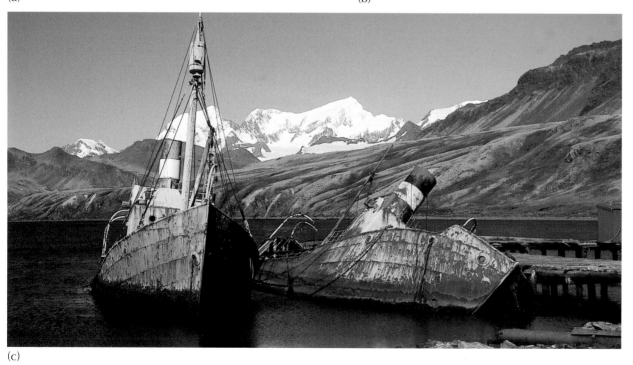
(c)

Figure 6.5 (a) A whale vertebra lying on the beach at Husvik whaling station. (b) Debris at the Stromness whaling station on South Georgia. (c) Two abandoned catcher boats at Grytviken on South Georgia.

138

The arguments about whaling are complicated and a list of the current member countries of the IWC is an interesting example of modern environmental politics. For a list of signatories and members, look at the IWC website at: www.iwcoffice.org/commission/members.htm (IWC, 2009).

■ What do you notice about some of the IWC member countries listed on the above website?

☐ A number, for instance, Austria, the Czech Republic, Hungary, Luxembourg, Mongolia, San Marino and Switzerland are landlocked, with no direct access to the sea. In addition, there are many small countries from the Caribbean and equatorial Africa.

Why would landlocked countries be members of an organisation that controls whaling on the high seas? Some environmentalists have alleged that Japan is linking aid to less developed countries with undertakings to persuade them to vote with Japan at the IWC. To complicate matters further although Iceland was an earlier member of the IWC it withdrew in 1992 citing disagreements with the scientific justification for the moratorium. It rejoined in 2002. Nevertheless, discussion regarding the moratorium between pro- and anti-whaling nations of the IWC remains a live issue because many scientists believe that minke whales could be sustainably harvested with a quota of several thousand animals a year.

6.5   A modern land rush: territorial conflicts in Antarctica

The territorial claim staked in Antarctica by Britain in 1908 was followed by claims from New Zealand (1923), France (1924), Australia (1933), Norway (1939), Chile (1940) and finally Argentina (1942). Unfortunately, the Argentinian, Chilean and British territorial claims overlapped on the Antarctic Peninsula (Figure 6.6). All of these countries believed they had a valid claim. In the case of the Antarctic Peninsula, Britain believed it discovered it and was administering part of it. Chile and Argentina used the idea of geographical proximity. With such competing claims could you say which country, if any, owned the Antarctic Peninsula?

The USA, which was present from almost the beginning of Antarctic exploration (see Table 4.1), was watching events closely. By 1924 there was pressure from the American public who wanted to know why the USA had not made a territorial claim. Charles Hughes, the US Secretary of State said:

> It is the opinion of this department that the discovery of land unknown to civilisation even when coupled with formal taking possession does not support the valid claim of sovereignty unless the discovery is followed by an *actual settlement* of the discovered country.

> (quoted in Sullivan, 1957, our italics)

Thus it became American policy not to recognise any country's Antarctic claims, but at the same time to reserve the right to make its own claim, and for its citizens to visit whenever they wanted. This policy is an extension of the 'high seas' argument that the Americans used to justify not allocating whale quotas to

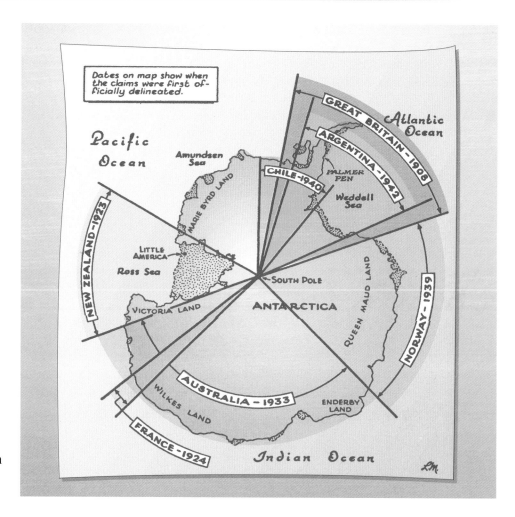

Figure 6.6 Locations and dates of territorial claims in Antarctica. This map was drawn in 1957 before the introduction of the Antarctic Treaty.

individual countries. The USA rapidly changed its policy in 1939 when Nazi Germany sent an expedition to Antarctica and announced its intention to make a territorial claim. (Germany was thwarted by the fact that its *Neu-Schwabenland* had already been claimed by Norway!) The US government responded by sending an expedition to the Antarctic. The Secretary of State specifically asked the members of the expedition to 'take appropriate steps such as dropping written claims from aeroplanes depositing such claims in cairns etc. which might persist in supporting a claim by the United States Government' (Sullivan, 1957). In effect this was a reversal of the original American policy.

Nobody was really sure how to make territorial claims legally binding in an uninhabited region. One certainty was that a permanent human presence would help any territorial claim and sovereignty would be enhanced if, for example, a country could prove it was administering the region perhaps through operating a postal service. Britain had already set up and operated the first Antarctic post office on South Georgia in 1909.

In World War II, the conflict eventually reached Antarctica when the German ship *Pinguin* arrived in the Southern Ocean. *Pinguin* had hidden guns and was disguised as a Greek cargo ship (painted in neutral colours) so that it could approach other shipping closely. In just 24 hours it captured three Norwegian factory ships and seven catcher boats off Queen Maud Land (see Figure 6.6).

This was most of the Norwegian whaling fleet and a valuable source of oil. To deny the use of the Antarctic Peninsula to the German raiders and to strengthen the British territorial claim, the British Admiralty sent a secret military expedition to the Antarctic in 1944 to establish a permanent presence. This was 'Operation Tabarin' (named after a Paris nightclub – Figure 6.7a) and it established the first permanent base in Antarctica (Base A) at Port Lockroy, with eight men (Figure 6.7b). Around the same time, the Royal Navy laid mines around the Kerguelen Islands (the islands are French Territory and, at about 69° E, they are on a similar latitude to South Georgia), where *Pinguin* had replenished food and supplies.

(a)

(b)

Figure 6.7   (a) Poster for the Tabarin nightclub in Paris, which inspired the name of the British military expedition. (b) British Base A, at Port Lockroy on the Antarctic Peninsula.

6.6   The post-war human invasion

After World War II, the British transferred operations to the civilian Falkland Islands Dependencies Survey (FIDS), which established more Antarctic bases (Figure 6.8). At the same time, the US Navy was looking for new challenges and organised 'Operation Highjump' (1946–7), the largest expedition ever to have gone to Antarctica. It is interesting to compare the British and American efforts. The British used two ships and placed generally fewer than 10 people at each base, but the American effort involved 13 warships, including an aircraft carrier, a submarine and almost 5000 men.

Not surprisingly, the other interested countries were rather concerned about this development, particularly as exploitable resources were being discovered at this time. *The New York Times* reported that 'Highjump' had discovered uranium deposits, although this was denied by Admiral Richard Byrd, the expedition

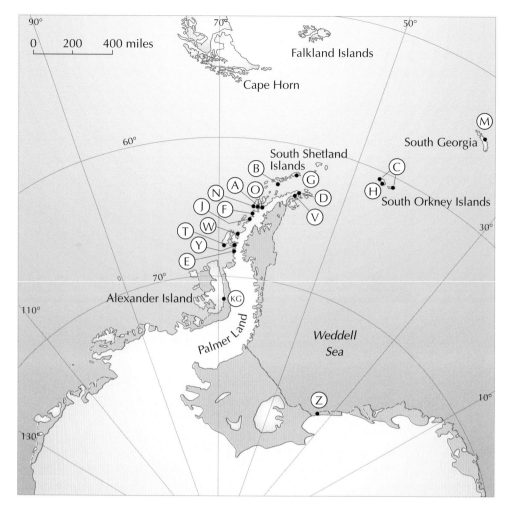

Figure 6.8 Locations of British bases (labelled by letter) in the British Antarctic Territory, established during and after World War II by 'Operation Tabarin' and the Falkland Islands Dependencies Survey. Each letter is the original identification label of the base: for example, 'A' points to the location of Base A at Port Lockroy.

leader. Another US admiral stated that the objectives for 'Highjump' included 'consolidating and extending United States sovereignty over the largest practicable area of the Antarctic continent'. But Byrd said the objectives were not diplomatic, scientific or economic; they were 'primarily of a military nature, that is to train naval personnel and to test ships, planes and equipment under frigid zone conditions' (quoted in Sullivan, 1957).

And so the first military invasion of Antarctica occurred. Although the personnel of 'Highjump' were the first to visit the South Pole since Captain Scott, the main contribution of the operation was the acquisition of aerial photographs of the coast (Figure 6.9). The reality was that the military card had been played and the Americans claimed they had discovered up to 700 000 square miles of land.

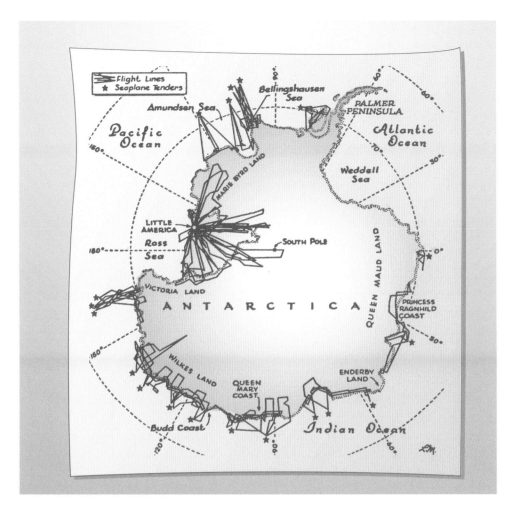

Figure 6.9   The extensive photographic surveying flights during 'Operation Highjump'.

6.7   Antarctic tempers rise

After operations 'Highjump' and 'Tabarin', the South American claimants were spurred into action. In one week in 1947, both Argentinian and Chilean ships sailed to Deception Island on the Antarctic Peninsula with the intention of setting up bases. One can only imagine what they thought when they found a British base already set up in the old whaling station. The situation was reaching a crisis point, with diplomatic notes being exchanged between London and Buenos Aires, and both countries sent warships south. In 1948, Chile upped the stakes with a visit by the President, the first Head of State to visit Antarctica. He said 'The bad habits of antiquated European imperialism is threatening with arms and violence to seize these lands of ours from Chile and America' (President Gabriel Gonzalez Videla, 1948, quoted in Sullivan, 1957).

Chile and Argentina then issued a joint declaration, saying that their rights to Antarctica were 'unquestionable'. With the start of the Cold War and attention elsewhere, the USA suggested 'some form of internationalization', but this was unacceptable to many parties. Numerous small incidents, some involving gunfire, continued and, in 1953, the British deported two Argentinians from Deception via the Falkland Islands. By this time something really had to be done. The only available option was the International Court of Justice in The Hague. In May 1955, Britain applied for arbitration and told the court that the continent was first discovered by Edward Bransfield on 30 January 1820, and that a British magistrate had been stationed at Deception Island during every whaling season from 1910 to 1930 – long before any other government had laid claim to the area. Chile and Argentina countered this by simply refusing to recognise the power of the court! The only real solution to avoid conflict lay in the USA's proposal to 'internationalise' Antarctica.

6.8   Peace breaks out: The International Geophysical Year of 1957–8

Figure 6.10   Logo of the International Geophysical Year 1957–8. The South Pole being inclined towards the viewer is designed to indicate the importance of Antarctica.

While the territorial disputes continued, Antarctica was becoming a continent for scientific study. There had already been two scientific events called 'International Polar Years' mainly concentrating on the Arctic – the first in 1882–3, and the second in 1932–3. The American physicist Lloyd Berkner (1905–1967) proposed a new global scientific expedition to study the Earth at the peak of the 11-year cycle of sunspot activity. This proposal led to the International Geophysical Year (IGY, 1957–8), whose logo is shown in Figure 6.10. It was the first international scientific programme and 67 countries were involved. Antarctic science is important since it is the perfect natural laboratory for studying, among other things, the aurora, cosmic rays, geomagnetism and, of course, glaciology. Although many countries had been working in Antarctica previously, there was no global perspective. For example, there was no network of weather stations and so no understanding of how the weather actually behaved around Antarctica. The massive increase in scientific effort during IGY made this network possible when 12 countries agreed to maintain year-round scientific stations.

The Antarctic component of the IGY was coordinated by the Special Committee for Antarctic Research (SCAR – later 'Special' was changed to 'Scientific'). SCAR helped to establish 44 Antarctic and sub-Antarctic research stations and chose the location of some key sites. These were the Antarctic Peninsula, the geographic South Pole (the USA set up the Amundsen–Scott Station), the Pole of Inaccessibility (the Soviet Sovetskaya Station) and the South Geomagnetic Pole (the Soviet Vostok Station). Simultaneously, the British Commonwealth Trans-Antarctic Expedition, led by Vivian Fuchs and Everest-conqueror Edmund Hillary, made a successful cross-Antarctic traverse, using both dogs and mechanised transport, which provided the first measurements of ice thickness all the way across the continent (Fuchs, 1982). The impact of the IGY on Antarctica was seen not only in the vast expansion in scientific output from the continent but also in the proliferation of Antarctic bases (Figure 6.11).

Figure 6.11   The expansion in the number of Antarctic research stations during the IGY 1957–8. (a) The locations of Antarctic research stations before the IGY. (b) The locations of Antarctic research stations during the IGY. The Amundsen–Scott base is at the South Pole, Vostok at the South Geomagnetic Pole and Sovetskaya at the Pole of Inaccessibility.

■   Look at Figure 6.11. How did the distribution of Antarctic research stations change during the IGY?

☐   More research stations were established, especially in the centre of the continent away from the coasts.

On the international stage at this time, the Cold War was in full swing with global peace threatened by the nuclear strategy of a mutually assured destruction, the Vietnam War, the building of the Berlin Wall, the Suez Crisis, and so on. However, in Antarctica there was cooperation – but no real solution. The situation at the end of the IGY was summed up perfectly by the journalist Walter Sullivan:

> Thus the situation stands today. There are postmasters with no mail to handle, Royal magistrates with no cases to try, brass plaques that look out over windswept mountains where men have visited but once. The flags, claim sheets, and other emblems dropped from the planes of various nations lie congealed into the crust over the continent. To those who have seen the vastness of the Antarctic ice sheet, the stark splendour of its mountains, incredible fury of its winds, these displays of national rivalry around its fringes seem strangely absurd.

> (Sullivan, 1957)

6.9   The Antarctic Treaty

If the scientific results from the IGY were important, the political outcome was momentous. Many countries that had never previously worked in Antarctica had established permanent bases and the USA suggested an international agreement be negotiated between the 12 countries who established year-round bases. These 12 countries met secretly in Washington every two weeks from the middle of 1958 until early 1959 to develop a solution. They produced the **Antarctic Treaty**, signed on 1 December 1959, which came into effect on 23 June 1961. The Treaty itself is rather short – it consists of only 14 articles. Some of them were deliberately imprecise and so open to problems with interpretation.

Perhaps the key article in the Antarctic Treaty is Article IV (see Box 6.1). It says, in an ambiguous way, that disputes of territorial sovereignty are insoluble and so should be put aside. Various authors have interpreted it as being either a step towards co-ownership of Antarctica or renunciation. The reality is that it puts *all* sovereignty claims into abeyance until a later and unspecified date. The Treaty itself has no expiry date and so will remain in force indefinitely; it also states that new decisions about international regulation south of 60° S must be made by 'unanimous agreement', that is, by consensus. But is a treaty with only 12 signatories a fair and practical way to determine the fate of a huge global resource?

Article IX of the Treaty allows other countries to become so-called Consultative Parties (CPs), if they engage in 'substantial scientific research activity' – but what does 'substantial' mean? Any country that signs the Treaty at this level can vote on future agreements. In addition, a second, lower level of membership was instigated for nations who, while not engaged in substantial research, agree to abide by the principles of the Treaty (called Non-Consultative Parties or NCPs). In June 2009 there were 28 CPs, and a further 18 NCPs.

Box 6.1 Article IV of the Antarctic Treaty

1 Nothing contained in the present Treaty shall be interpreted as:

   (a) a renunciation by any Contracting Party of previously asserted rights of or claims to territorial sovereignty in Antarctica;

   (b) a renunciation or diminution by any Contracting Party of any basis of claim to territorial sovereignty in Antarctica which it may have whether as a result of its activities or those of its nationals in Antarctica, or otherwise;

   (c) prejudicing the position of any Contracting Party as regards its recognition or non-recognition of any other State's rights of, or claim, or basis of claim to territorial sovereignty in Antarctica.

2 No acts or activities taking place while the present Treaty is in force shall constitute a basis for asserting, supporting or denying a claim to territorial sovereignty in Antarctica or create any rights of sovereignty in Antarctica. No new claim, or enlargement of an existing claim, to territorial sovereignty in Antarctica shall be asserted while the present Treaty is in force.

It can take a long time to reach consensus decisions. Further, all countries have the same voting rights as each other whatever their budget for Antarctic research: for example, the USA has a budget of about £200 million per year whereas New Zealand has a budget of about £2 million per year but each country has one vote. Some countries probably have more influence than others in what is now called the **Antarctic Treaty System** (ATS), but consensus can break down and an individual country can decide an issue.

Because countries can become a CP by setting up a year-round Antarctic research station, there has been a proliferation of bases on the tip of the Antarctic Peninsula, for example on King George Island (Figure 6.12). This island is easily accessible to non-icebreaking ships (Bransfield found it in a wooden sailing ship) and building a base there does not require sophisticated technology. In the words of the Polish Academy of Sciences, it is now 'somewhat overcrowded', with nine stations being present over the winter of 2000 (some right next to each other), and in summer the number rises to at least 10, although usually more. Four of the countries there do not work elsewhere in the Antarctic and the obvious question is are they doing the same 'research' as other stations on King George Island?

Figure 6.12 Winter stations on King George Island on the Antarctic Peninsula in 2000. Could meteorological data collected at Great Wall station be very different from that collected at Frei?

Despite these problems, overall the Treaty has been a success and there has been no Antarctic military conflict. The Treaty has also led the way in international environmental law with the adoption of a further four agreements (Table 6.1).

Table 6.1 International agreements adopted under the Antarctic Treaty System.

Agreement	Year
Agreed Measures for the Conservation of Antarctic Fauna and Flora	1964
Convention for the Conservation of Antarctic Seals (CCAS)	1972
Convention for the Conservation of Antarctic Marine Living Resources (CCAMLR)	1982
Protocol on Environmental Protection to the Antarctic Treaty	1998

Each of the agreements in Table 6.1 was a major step forward in the governance of Antarctica. The Agreed Measures covered one of the most important environmental issues by banning the importation of non-indigenous species. It also stated that animals could not be killed without a permit, and allowed for the designation of specially protected areas. Today, this agreement has been superseded by the Protocol on Environmental Protection (1998). Like the Antarctic Treaty, the CCAS applies south of 60° S and its purpose was to protect seals if sealing was to recommence, and to completely prohibit the killing of Ross and Antarctic fur seals. The CCAMLR is very different and its boundary is not 60 °S, but the polar front – much further north than the other agreements. It controls Antarctic fisheries using what is called an ecosystem approach rather than a straight quota system. This is described in more detail in the next section. The Protocol on Environmental Protection has an interesting history. It arose from the demise of another convention which, despite being reached by consensus, was publicly and painfully ended.

6.10 The failure of the Convention on the Regulation of Antarctic Mineral Resource Activities (CRAMRA)

The Antarctic Treaty does not mention mineral resources. This omission is surprising since the earliest explorers found coal, and regions of Antarctica are geologically very similar to the mineral-rich areas of South America, South Africa and Australia (Figure 4.14a). However, potential mining activity was not regulated until 1970 when Britain and New Zealand first raised the issue after being approached by oil companies. The Treaty nations agreed a mining moratorium until a comprehensive agreement could be reached and, by 1988, the Convention on the Regulation of Antarctic Mineral Resource Activities (CRAMRA) was tabled. As this agreement had been reached by consensus, it should have been a formality for the countries to sign and ratify it. Exploration and mining were to be allowed but with strict controls. Before any major activity, the environmental impact would be reviewed, and no activity would be allowed unless all of the Treaty nations agreed that there would be no risk to the environment. Unfortunately, the clause that stopped mining would only come into play if there were 'significant' adverse environmental effects. Many environmental groups were fundamentally opposed to mining and they launched a major international campaign to stop the CRAMRA being ratified.

6.10.1 Greenpeace goes to Antarctica

The world had not stood still since the Treaty was agreed and environmental groups were making their presence felt in Antarctic affairs. The environmental group Greenpeace had been on the global scene for a couple of decades and had a reputation for high-impact environmental protests, for example against whaling and the testing of nuclear weapons. As the organisation (and of course its funding) grew, it campaigned on wider issues, and what could be bigger than the violation of the 'last wilderness'? Greenpeace could have just publicised the issue of Antarctica, but it was much bolder and decided to send its own expedition to the region and in 1987 built an Antarctic base (Figure 6.13).

Figure 6.13 World Park Base set up by Greenpeace in 1987 on Ross Island.

Although this expedition was certainly not the first private one to visit Antarctica, Greenpeace was the first environmental non-governmental organisation (NGO) to do so, and ultimately its aim was to have Antarctica declared an international 'World Park'. It even tried to become a Treaty CP by conducting scientific research at its base, and onboard its ship, the MV Greenpeace. However, Article XIII of the ATS makes it clear that Treaty CP membership is only open to 'any state which is a Member of the United Nations' – and of course an NGO is not a state.

The Greenpeace principles for the 'World Park' were simple:

1   The wilderness values of Antarctica should be protected;

2   There should be complete protection for Antarctic wildlife (though limited fishing would be permissible);

3   Antarctica should remain a zone of limited scientific activity with cooperation and coordination between scientists of all nations;

4   Antarctica should remain a zone of peace, free of all weapons.

(May, 1988)

At first sight the principles seem sensible, but look again at the language. Greenpeace had previously criticised the vague and ambiguous terms in the ATS – which it still publicly supported – but it had made the same mistake itself. What exactly are 'wilderness values'? Despite these problems the campaign was a great success and Greenpeace brilliantly exploited the public perception of Antarctica. As well as building an environmentally friendly base, it visited and inspected existing research stations and was shocked by what it saw. Greenpeace's publicity machine highlighted violations of the Antarctic Treaty with photographic evidence of rubbish dumps full of non-biodegradable waste such as plastics, metals and even trucks. It also filmed some spectacular footage of French workers blowing up penguins while building a runway at Dumont d'Urville (66 °S 140 °E). By suggesting that previous agreements (even ones they publicly thought enforced good standards) were not good enough, how could people trust the CRAMRA?

As mentioned above, the publicity was highly successful and not just in influencing public opinion. In 1981 there were 25 signatories to the Treaty but, by 1988, when the CRAMRA was ready to be signed, numbers had risen to 38. At the same time, countries that were not part of the ATS (e.g. Malaysia) were arguing in the UN that Antarctica was 'the common heritage of mankind'.

How could 38 nations decide its fate? In 1989, the Argentinian ship *Bahia Paraiso* was wrecked on the Antarctic Peninsula. This event demonstrated the vulnerability of the region to oil pollution and thus increased the pressure on all countries in Antarctica.

CRAMRA was built on consensus by the Treaty countries – they only had to sign and ratify it. But, by now, public opinion was against CRAMRA. The first country to refuse was Australia, followed by France. However, New Zealand finally finished off CRAMRA; it had already signed but refused to ratify the Treaty. The need for 'unanimous agreement' torpedoed CRAMRA and brought about crisis in the Antarctic Treaty System. Consensus had been broken and the ensuing vigorous public debate led to Britain and Chile calling for a special Treaty meeting to discuss comprehensive measures to protect the Antarctic environment. The ATS countries responded by agreeing the Protocol on Environmental Protection in 1991, with most parties signing immediately. However, it took until 1998 to come into force.

In an ironic twist, many of the pioneering environmental controls in CRAMRA were simply transferred to the Protocol. The latter is a very tough international agreement and it has had a tremendous effect. Antarctica was designated a 'natural reserve devoted to science' with various consequences. On the question of mining, the Protocol bans all 'mineral resource activity' except genuine scientific research. It banished huskies from the region by 1994 as they were non-indigenous. All rubbish in certain categories now has to be removed, and the discharge of waste materials into the sea is not allowed. There has also been a very large and expensive clean-up of abandoned bases.

An **Environmental Impact Assessment** (EIA) is now required for *any* activity in Antarctica, and activities can only proceed if there is sufficient information to determine that their impact is acceptable. Essentially, this EIA requirement is the effective gatekeeper of Antarctica. Any activity that has an impact considered more than minor must undergo a **Comprehensive Environmental Evaluation** (CEE), which is then reviewed under the ATS system.

Arguably, the rejection of CRAMRA – an agreement that would have allowed mineral exploitation – has created a much tougher system that affects *all* Antarctic activities from tourism to science. However, the mining issue is not permanently buried as it has only been prohibited for 50 years. Discussion will probably recommence by about 2035.

6.11   Antarctica today

Antarctica is now well governed and has some of the toughest environmental regulations in the world. Although science remains the dominant activity, this final stage of our Antarctic journey examines how the agreements of the ATS control current activities.

6.11.1   CCAMLR and ecosystem management

A traditional fishery, such as those in the North Atlantic, is regulated by what is called the single-species approach. This system bases catch quotas on estimates of the abundance of individual species. However, there have been many cases where single-species fisheries have collapsed despite the quota system, from the Antarctic whales, to the Canadian cod fishery and North Sea herring. The approach has two basic flaws (assuming everyone involved is honest). The first is that governments tend to set targets rather than strict limits – after all, it would be a shame to throw back what you have already caught if you had brought up too much. A more serious deficiency is that the system does not take into account any interaction between species.

■ Recall the example in Chapter 3 (Section 3.2) where interactions between fish species are the suspected cause of an overfished resource failing to recover. What was the resource and what kind of ecological interaction was involved?

☐ The resource was Atlantic cod in Newfoundland. Their recovery is possibly inhibited by an increase in smaller predatory fish that eat cod fry (see Box 3.1).

In contrast, the CCAMLR (Table 6.1) controls the exploitation of the Antarctic marine environment using an ecosystem approach that is based on the relationship between all the different components in the ecosystem. It starts by defining the northern boundaries of the Antarctic ecosystem as the polar front, which is much further north than the traditional 60 °S latitude and includes South Georgia and Kerguelen, and the whole ecosystem within this area is relevant. For example, if you were setting a catch limit on krill, you would have to base this value on an understanding of *all* the ways in which the different organisms in the ecosystem rely on it. You can see that this would be a complicated process because krill is a keystone species with many dependent predators (Chapter 5). You must also understand how changing the environment could affect krill numbers *before* setting a Total Allowable Catch (TAC) based on the 'precautionary principle'. According to this principle, the fishery must be sustainable with the effects of dependent species (e.g. penguins and seals in the case of krill) being understood before a fishery can begin. The CCAMLR has set a TAC for krill of 5 million tonnes per year using this approach, but the current catch is only approximately 2% of this value with just over 100 000 tonnes fished in 2007 though plans to take up to 750 million tonnes were disclosed at the 2007 meeting of the CCAMLR. The ecosystem approach is progressive (even Greenpeace supports it) and, within the next 30 years, the rest of the North Atlantic fisheries may be governed in the same way; 'may' because the countries that fish in the North Atlantic do not have the foundation of the ATS to build on and so it will be a difficult, or perhaps impossible, political process.

The CCAMLR ecosystem approach should lead to an expectation that some species increase in numbers when their predators, or their competitors for food, are harvested.

■ Which other Antarctic animals could have exploited any 'extra' food made available by the drastic reduction in whale numbers?

☐ Penguins, albatross and seals (Chapter 5).

As noted earlier, in 1958 there were fewer than 100 pairs of fur seals left on South Georgia. However, since seal hunting stopped, the seal population increase has been staggering and, by the end of the 20th century, there were probably over 1 million fur seals on the island. This extraordinary recovery has been attributed to a combination of the protection of the seals by the CCAS, but probably more importantly to the extra availability of food caused by the reduction in whale numbers. Although the cause is uncertain, the effect is clear: on South Georgia and other sub-Antarctic islands seals are expanding into areas once inhabited by other animals such as penguins, and are possibly driving them away through competition. The ecosystem is rapidly changing, and there are now some seal experts who believe that the only way to prevent numbers increasing even further would be to amend the CCAS to allow fur seals to be culled. But could you see that being allowed?

Another problem with the CCAMLR approach is highlighted by the wealth of unprotected resources. In most parts of the world, fisheries protection is a common naval role but in the CCAMLR region there are few such ships, and the 60 °S line presents a problem because of the non-military requirement. Fish species such as the Patagonian toothfish (*Dissostichus eleginoides*) and the Antarctic toothfish (*Dissostichus mawsoni*) are today's 'gold mines', and the campaign against pirate fishing is very active. One Greenpeace press release was entitled 'Business as usual for CCAMLR as Antarctica's fish and wildlife hang in the balance'. If you think this is overstated, you can visit the CCAMLR website and download its reports. The scale of the problem has been clear for some time; for example, its 2001 report stated:

> The Chair of the Scientific Committee advised the Commission that the catches reported from [an area outside the CCAMLR region] were not credible. Therefore the Committee 'concluded that practically all the toothfish catches reported from [this area] represent catches taken as a result of ... fishing ... inside the Convention Area'.

> (CCAMLR, 2001, paragraph 5.4)

However, the CCAMLR regulations call for a TAC to be set based on what is *reported* to have been caught within the Convention area, even though this may be a serious underestimate of the actual catch.

■   What would be the effect of setting a TAC based on actual catches rather than reported catches?

☐   The TAC would be much lower.

Even legal toothfish fishing causes problems because the fish are caught using longline hooks rather than nets. The ships trail thousands of baited hooks on lines many kilometres long. Unfortunately, seabirds dive to take the bait as the hooks are deployed, become trapped and are dragged underwater and drowned. The problems of longlining are not limited to the CCAMLR region because this method is used all over the world. However, for species such as albatrosses, which like blue whales are long-lived and slow to reproduce, the attrition rate has been staggering. A recent census showed a drop in albatross numbers of 76 000 in just a 5-year period in the Falkland Islands. The same pattern seems to be appearing in South Georgia and Kerguelen. The CCAMLR has taken a series of measures to reduce this problem of 'bird bycatch' but a global solution is required if seabirds such as the albatross are to be saved.

6.11.2   Research

Science in Antarctica has continued to develop and expand. Many countries have large, year-round research programmes and, over the years, Antarctic science has contributed much to our understanding of how the Earth works. At the beginning of the 21st century, this research is contributing to an understanding of how other planets may work; for example, the endolithic communities in the Dry Valleys (Figure 5.5) are thought to represent possible life forms that may be found on Mars. The most famous Antarctic scientific advance to date is considered to be the discovery of the **ozone hole** (Box 6.2) by the British Antarctic Survey in 1985.

Box 6.2 The Antarctic ozone hole

Ozone (O_3) is a gas that is both created and destroyed by natural processes. It exists at low levels in the atmosphere, and the stratosphere ozone molecules protect life on Earth by absorbing ultraviolet light that can damage living cells. Unfortunately, in the second half of the 20th century, the introduction of synthetic chemical compounds such as chlorofluorocarbons (CFCs) (once used in refrigerators and aerosols) and halons (in fire extinguishers) upset the natural balance. The compounds break up the ozone through complex chemical reactions and remove it from the atmosphere. This process, when combined with the very cold winter atmospheric conditions around Antarctica, creates a situation where ozone is destroyed very rapidly. Although we began using these CFCs and halons at the end of World War II, it was not until 1985 that scientists at the British Antarctic

Survey demonstrated the presence of a region of very low ozone concentration over Antarctica at the end of the Antarctic winter. This 'hole' has been observed every year since, with the largest being recorded in September 2006 (Figure 6.14).

Scientific proof that the ozone depletion was derived from human activity was the first conclusive evidence of our negative impact on the whole planet. The international community rapidly responded and quickly adopted what became known as the Montreal Protocol to protect the ozone layer. The manufacture of CFCs and halons has been banned but, unfortunately, these chemicals last for decades in the atmosphere so it will take at least another 50 years for the ozone levels to recover.

Figure 6.14   Satellite map of the largest ozone hole recorded over Antarctica, September 2006, from data collected with the Total Ozone Mapping Spectrometer (TOMS). The blue and purple colours are where there is the least ozone, and the greens, yellows and reds are where there is more ozone.

More recently, perhaps, the most exciting event has been the discovery of vast freshwater lakes deep beneath the Antarctic ice cap. The largest of these lakes is buried 3.75 km beneath the Russian Vostok Station and it was mapped in 1996 by Martin Siegert, a British scientist (Siegert, 2001). It became known as Lake Vostok and is approximately 240 km × 50 km and up to 1000 m deep. This lake may be hundreds of thousands, or even millions, of years old, and it was formed because the ice is so heavy that in some places at the bottom of the sheet it melts because of the huge pressure on it from above. Scientists believe that the lake water has been out of contact with the atmosphere for over 500 000 years and could therefore contain unique microbes and life forms. However, Vostok also has another focus for research. In the 1980s, work began to drill a deep core of ice to study trapped gases to help reconstruct the past climate of the Earth. You will learn more about the results of this research in Book 3.

■   Would the climate scientists have had to prepare an EIA?

☐   No, they started their work before the Protocol came into force in 1998.

Siegert's work on Lake Vostok had an immediate impact. NASA became interested in testing the technology used to sample the lake because conditions could be similar to those found on Europa, an ice-covered moon of Jupiter. But the lake is pristine and, with no EIA, the climate scientists were drilling towards it using a mixture of kerosene and anti-freeze to lubricate the drill. Penetration of the lake would certainly create an environmental impact that would be greater than 'minor or transitory'. According to the Protocol there should be a CEE for the ATS to review, and in 1998 drilling was stopped at a depth of 3623 m – within 150 m of the lake. Russia submitted a draft CEE to the ATS in 2002 proposing further drilling, but it is controversial and drilling is unlikely to go ahead at present. Drilling will probably take place eventually but new methods will have to be developed to avoid polluting Lake Vostok.

6.11.3   Antarctic tourism

Antarctica has been a fast-growing tourist destination since the late 1950s when both Argentina and Chile took a few hundred fare-paying passengers to the South Shetland Islands on naval ships.

■   Why would these countries take tourists to Antarctica?

☐   It was an attempt to demonstrate sovereignty.

The tourist industry developed a style called 'expedition cruising', whereby tour companies took cruise ships south and employed scientists to educate the passengers about Antarctica. It seemed to work and tourist numbers steadily increased. By the 1980s there were about 1000 people visiting the area each year, even as the CRAMRA negotiations were continuing. When tourists visited research stations they were as horrified as Greenpeace at what they saw and naturally voiced their protests loudly (Figure 6.15).

Some countries prevented tourists from visiting their bases altogether, but this was difficult to achieve as the Treaty provides freedom of access and many bases were already abandoned. Tourist numbers continued to rise and, as the industry

Figure 6.15   Tourists walk past materials abandoned by a national Antarctic programme.

developed, the tour operators formed their own Antarctic NGO in 1991 – the International Association of Antarctica Tour Operators (IAATO) – with the aim of responsible private sector travel in Antarctica. The IATTO now has 46 members and attends Treaty meetings as expert observers.

The Protocol on Environmental Protection requires that abandoned bases and waste dumps in Antarctica must be 'cleared up'. For example, the British Antarctic Survey (BAS) and the UK Antarctic Heritage Trust (a charity) carried out a spectacular job of restoring Port Lockroy (Base A, Figure 6.7b). By converting a derelict station into a museum, they have created one of the most popular visitor sites in Antarctica.

The impact of tourism is now on the agenda: for example, dealing with the abandoned debris and waste seen in Figures 6.5b, 6.15 and 6.16. But more

Figure 6.16   Waste awaiting collection and removal from an Antarctic base.

importantly, what about other effects such as tourists visiting penguin colonies? Most cruise ships only visit the northern end of the Antarctic Peninsula on short 10-day trips. This means that they repeatedly visit the same sites (the data are collected by IAATO and presented at ATS meetings). Port Lockroy (Figure 6.7b) has been in the top five most visited sites since data collection started, and in 2001–2, almost 6400 people landed there. BAS investigations showed that tourism was having no effect on the penguins there when compared with undisturbed regions nearby. Similar work has concluded that the effects of tourists are negligible when compared with long-term natural environmental changes. These results are not surprising as IAATO provides its passengers with comprehensive guidelines on responsible behaviour that have been agreed by the Antarctic Treaty countries. These guidelines are combined with a high staff – passenger ratio on landings, which ensures proper control. Self-regulation appears to have worked so far, and any adverse effects of Antarctic tourism seem to have been minimal.

■ Why do you think self-regulation appears to be working?

☐ The tourists are visiting a region where they *believe* they have to act in a responsible manner and are strictly controlled by the tour operators.

In the early years of the 21st century, a traveller has many choices connected with Antarctic tourism. You could go on a cruise ship, a small yacht, or even fly to the South Pole. The IAATO has estimated that by 2010 there could be more than 25 ships operating in the Antarctic, not counting private yachts. This number could mean up to 20 000 people visiting the area each year (Figure 6.17). If self-regulation continues to work, there should not be a problem. Of course, the situation could rapidly change if a large cruise ship was wrecked – something that is perhaps not so unlikely as the Southern Ocean is generally poorly surveyed. Any resulting pollution or loss of life could certainly change public opinion.

6.12   Conclusions

The Antarctic continent was probably discovered in the late 18th century, but the first huts and settlements were built much more recently. This chapter began with the depressing story of the slaughter of the great whales and the potential military conflict over territorial claims. Since then, however, the story has been generally positive. Given a remote and special region, little historical baggage and a pressing need for conservation, countries have developed the ATS – a system based on consensus. Now, in theory, even the smallest country can have a say on Antarctic issues. But is this really the case? A look at the membership of the ATS shows that there are only two CPs from the less developed world that are not from South America (China and India), and no African members apart from South Africa. We also have to ask whether the Treaty needs to be updated? For example, is the 60° S latitude a sensible limit for the Antarctic Treaty area? Figure 5.1 shows that the polar waters extend much further north. The CCAMLR recognised this 20 years after the Treaty was signed and defined a much larger region. Would a more northerly limit have made any difference?

Figure 6.17   Modern ship-based Antarctic tourism. (a) The restored British Antarctic research station at Port Lockroy, now operating as a museum. In beautiful scenery and weather, some tourists interact with the penguins by taking photographs, and others return to the ship with bags of shopping. (b) The radio room in Port Lockroy. (c) A lecturer (with the yellow radio) telling tourists about a historic food cache. (d) Tourists learning about whaling.

It certainly could have made a difference in terms of military action. During the Falklands War in 1982, Argentina invaded South Georgia and, in this particular battle, several Argentinian soldiers died and there was one British injury. An undefended BAS base was also captured. However, south of 60° S, both countries were still working together. Within 22 days, South Georgia was recaptured. Britain was aware that Argentina had built a base on Thule (59.5° S, 27.4° W, the most southerly of the South Sandwich Islands) and they set out to take control.

British troops removed what diplomats had described as the 'illegal occupation' in June 1982, to much Argentinian protest at the UN. The British then returned in February 1983 to blow up the Argentine base. We cannot predict what could have happened if the ATS limit was similar to the CCAMLR one, but there was no military action – and cooperation continued – south of the Treaty boundary.

In terms of resource management, the CCAMLR was the first international fisheries treaty to use an ecosystem approach for sustainable development. It is a model for other areas and, but for illegal fishing, would be even more successful.

With the introduction of the Environmental Protocol and the rise of tourism, activities in Antarctica have completely changed. You may believe tourism should not have been allowed because of potential environmental impacts, but could you say its impact would be greater than that of the various research stations on King George Island?

Overall, Antarctica is an amazing example of the effect of globalisation on the environmental web. Look at the contrast between the images of Antarctic exploration at the beginning of the 20th century (Figure 4.8) and those of tourists at an Antarctic base by the end of that century (Figure 6.17). The world has changed, and now anyone with sufficient money can visit Antarctica. Globalisation has changed the continent from a remote and little known region, supplying huge and unsustainable supplies of seals and whales, into a place that is considered a 'barometer' for the planet's health. People may deny that anthropogenic climate change is responsible for ice-shelf collapse, but who could deny the existence of the Antarctic ozone hole and its anthropogenic cause?

You have seen that the wealth of information and data available on the internet is staggering, but it is often difficult to find the information you really need, and then determine how accurate it is. The hope is that when you are faced with any question, you can now gather information from the internet and draw your own conclusions, rather than just take it as read. If you want to know about the problems being discussed by the ATS or with the CCAMLR, why take an NGO's word for it when you can read their papers yourself? Combine this information with your knowledge of how ecosystems operate and you can identify problems yourself. Providing you have the background knowledge to tie it together, the possibilities are practically endless.

6.13   Summary of Chapter 6

6.1 The unsustainable exploitation of seal and whale populations in Antarctica in the early 20th century led to a steep decline in the numbers of these animals.

6.2 The Discovery Investigations research programme, set up to examine the impact of unsustainable exploitation, was instrumental in advancing our understanding of the Antarctic marine environment, ecosystem and ocean circulation.

6.3 The International Whaling Commission (IWC) was set up as an international attempt to manage the whaling industry. Despite whale numbers severely declining after World War II, it took until 1984 before a moratorium on whaling was implemented. In 2008 this moratorium was still in place.

6.4 Several countries made territorial claims in Antarctica before World War II, but the first permanent base in Antarctica was not established until 1944, by the British.

6.5 No country could work out how to enforce sovereignty in Antarctica. With the American 'Operation Highjump', and the expansion of the Falkland Islands Dependencies Survey (FIDS), tension increased.

6.6 Internationalisation occurred through the International Geophysical Year of 1957–8. The result of this scientific event was the Antarctic Treaty System (ATS).

6.7 The Antarctic Treaty has 12 original signatories, although today the numbers have increased to 46. Decisions on Antarctic matters south of 60° S are reached through the ATS by consensus between the 28 CPs.

6.8 The ATS has introduced four further pieces of legislation determining governance of Antarctica. The fourth – the Protocol on Environmental Protection to the Antarctic Treaty (1998) – was introduced because of the failure of a convention on mining (CRAMRA). This protocol now acts as a gatekeeper to Antarctica and means that an EIA must be prepared for all activities.

6.9 Antarctica is now a region of science and tourism. The resource exploitation is fishing activity, which is controlled by the CCAMLR.

Questions for Chapter 6

Question 6.1

Explain what is meant by the ozone hole. Why is the ozone hole a problem?

Once you have completed the questions for Chapter 6, you should go to the course website and do the activities associated with this part of the chapter.

Question 6.2

What is the difference between an Environmental Impact Assessment and a Comprehensive Environmental Evaluation?

Question 6.3

What is the difference between the Antarctic Treaty and the Antarctic Treaty System?

Question 6.4

Which of the following statements is *false*?

(a) Whale populations in Antarctica targeted by human hunters declined because the predation rate was greater than the whales' reproduction rates.

(b) The introduction of factory ships in the 1920s allowed a huge increase in the number of whales that could be caught in Antarctica because the whalers were no longer restricted to particular areas.

(c) Whalers had a large effect on terrestrial ecosystems in Antarctica as well as on marine ones.

(d) In the first half of the 20th century, the Norwegian government controlled the whaling industry in Antarctica, and so collected large amounts of tax revenue from it.

(e) During the period when whales were hunted intensively, population numbers of larger whales fell first because these were the most profitable to catch.

(f) When larger whales became scarce, whalers shifted to hunting ever smaller whales.

Question 6.5

Which of the following could have helped to *increase* whale population numbers in the Antarctic, which would have tended to *decrease* them, and which would probably have had no effect?

(a) Whaling

(b) The setting up of the International Whaling Commission in 1946

(c) The moratorium on whaling declared by the IWC in 1982

(d) The decline of seal populations

(e) The lack of profit available from hunting when whale populations are very small

(f) The readmission of Iceland to the IWC

Question 6.6

Which two of the following statements are *false*?

(a) No one knows for certain who discovered Antarctica.

(b) The British Government claimed ownership of the Antarctic Peninsula from 20° W to 80° W in 1908.

(c) Britain, New Zealand and France were the first countries to make territorial claims in Antarctica.

(d) Captain James Cook made the first landing on South Georgia and claimed the island for Britain.

(e) Most territorial claims in Antarctica are based on geographical proximity or claims of first discovery.

(f) Territorial claims made before the Antarctic Treaty came into effect were recognised by international law as long as they were supported by human habitation.

(g) Most whalers on South Georgia were Norwegian.

(h) The Discovery Investigations established the continuous nature of the polar front around Antarctica, and included studies of the food, life history and habits of whales and seals, the life cycle of krill, and the circulation of the Southern Ocean.

(i) The International Whaling Commission was set up to ensure the orderly development of the whaling industry.

(j) The USA used 'Operation Highjump', which placed nearly 5000 men in Antarctica, to reinforce its territorial claims.

(k) The first long-term research programme in Antarctica was set up by Argentina.

Question 6.7

Name the most important research initiative to take place in Antarctica (a) before 1950 and (b) after 1950. What was the significance of each initiative?

Question 6.8

Why could it be said that the following are limitations of the Antarctic Treaty System? Could it be argued that any of these are strengths?

(a) The articles of the Antarctic Treaty have been written in a deliberately imprecise way.

(b) Decisions can only be reached by consensus.

(c) The Antarctic Treaty covers the area south of 60 °S.

Question 6.9

Which of the following statements is *false*?

(a) The Agreed Measures for the Conservation of Antarctic Fauna and Flora banned the importation of non-indigenous species to Antarctica.

(b) The CCAMLR sets fishing quotas in the region south of the polar front.

(c) An ecosystem approach is used to set fishing quotas in Antarctica.

(d) The Greenpeace campaign in the 1980s was a major cause of the failure of the CRAMRA.

(e) The introduction of the Protocol on Environmental Protection to the Antarctic Treaty led to a massive clean-up of Antarctica, banished huskies, and introduced EIAs and CEEs.

(f) The Protocol on Environmental Protection to the Antarctic Treaty finally resolved the debate on whether to allow mining for mineral resources that had been going on through the 1970s and 1980s by bringing in a permanent ban.

(g) The ecosystem approach sets a catch quota based on an understanding of all the ways in which different animals in the whole ecosystem rely on the particular species that is to be harvested.

(h) A quota (TAC) can be set that is sustainable because the ecosystem approach takes account of all the factors affecting the numbers of a harvested species.

Question 6.10

Name two major scientific discoveries in Antarctica since 1970 and briefly explain their relevance.

Question 6.11

Which of the following statements is *false*?

(a) There has been a decline in the numbers of penguins in a colony at Port Lockroy visited by tourists, compared with an undisturbed colony.

(b) Tourism in Antarctica began in the late 1950s.

(c) The IAATO provides its passengers with guidelines for environmentally responsible tourism that have been agreed by the Antarctic Treaty nations.

(d) Tourism in Antarctica has so far been successfully self-regulated.

(e) By 2010, there could be 25 000 visitors per year, compared with about 1000 per year in the 1970s.

References

CCAMLR (2001) *Commission for the Conservation of Antarctic Marine Living Resources: Report of the Twentieth Meeting of the Commission*, Hobart, Australia, 22 October–2 November 2001.

Colonial Office, UK (1920) *Report of the Interdepartmental Committee on Research and Development in the Dependencies of the Falklands Islands*, Command paper no. 657, 164 pp., London, HMSO.

Fuchs, V. (1982) *Office and Men*, Oswestry, Anthony Nelson.

Hardy, A. (1967) *Great Waters*, London, Collins.

Headland, R.K. (1984) *The Island of South Georgia*, Cambridge, Cambridge University Press.

Hough, R. (1994) *Captain James Cook*, London, Hodder and Stoughton.

IWC (International Whaling Commission) (2009) [online], www.iwcoffice.org (Accessed 4 February 2009).

Jackson, G. (1978) *The British Whaling Trade*, London, Adam and Charles Black.

Lucas, C.E. and Cole, H.A. (1965) in Mackintosh, N.A. (ed.) *The Stocks of Whales*, London, Fishing News.

May, J. (1988) *The Greenpeace Book of Antarctica*, London, Dorling Kindersley.

Siegert, M.J. (2001) 'Physical, chemical and biological processes in Lake Vostok and the Antarctic subglacial lakes', *Nature*, vol. 414, pp. 603–9.

Sullivan, W. (1957) *Quest for a Continent*, London, Secker & Warburg.

Conclusion

Did it strike you as strange that people on coral atolls should be worrying about what is happening to the ice shelves of Antarctica? What may be even stranger is the fact that, in today's world, people on tropical islands and atolls worrying about Antarctica is starting to seem quite normal. This says a lot about just how globalised the world has become, and about the role of environmental issues in this globalisation.

This course has started not in your own backyard, nor even in the region or country where you probably live. In different ways, tropical islands and the continent of Antarctica are about as far from living in the northern temperate latitudes as you can get. For many centuries the existence of small oceanic islands and the great southern continent were the object of speculation and fantasy for European people. Later, as they were pinned down to actual locations on the world map, they became places of scientific interest and armchair curiosity. However, it is only in recent decades that the fate of tropical islands and of the ice-covered southern continent has taken on a direct and pressing relevance to ordinary people living thousands of miles away. In some senses, our attention is now held by Antarctica and islands such as the Maldives as if they were our own backyard.

Today, there is a growing awareness that threats to biodiversity have a meaning and a significance far beyond the immediate location in which endangered species are found. To an even greater extent, global environmental changes, such as climate change and the thinning of the ozone layer, are giving rise to a new sense of connectedness to faraway places. While the human contribution to global changes may be on a scale without precedent, the point made throughout this book is that distant regions around the globe have been linked for millions of years before any human impact. Indeed, the very existence of these ancient and ongoing patterns of teleconnection between regions and around the entire planet transmits human impacts from one part of the globe to another.

Recently, social scientists have noted that the tendency of environmental problems to spill over national boundaries is changing the way people think about countries, leading us away from a sense of bounded and limited spaces to thinking about the world as a single, interconnected place. This view has emerged from focusing predominantly on environmental issues such as acid rain and leakage from nuclear power plants that have arisen over the past few decades in the most developed parts of the world. While the idea of environmental problems overflowing nation states is correct in some senses, it is also misleading, for it gives an impression that national boundaries came first, and the environmental issues that overran them came later.

This book took a broader approach to environmental issues, looking deeper into the past and further afield. As the evidence implies, environmental problems pre-date the arrangement of countries as they now stand. The division of the world into 'sovereign' states goes back at most a few hundred years, much less in some regions. But environmental disturbance recedes into a distant and prehistoric past. Wherever human beings have moved away from the ecosystems they are familiar with and into novel ecosystems, they have tended to take their old ways of viewing and doing things with them. The likely result has been environmental disturbance and, after this disruption, a long and usually painful period of adjustment.

Over much of the world, the evidence of these periods of environmental change is buried beneath layers of physical and cultural change. But this is much less the case in those places that have been, until relatively recently, on the edge of the 'known world'. The last new lands and seas to be opened to human intervention provide some of the clearest and most dramatic records of rapid environmental change. The impact of settlement on small island ecosystems and the overexploitation of the southern polar regions, as this book showed, brings into sharp relief the problem of environmental disturbance as an outcome of the lack of adjustment between human practices and ecosystems. But these cases also offer some vital insights on the adjustment process: the business of learning and adapting to new ecosystems.

You have also seen that adjustment is not simply a process of learning to stay in the bounds of the ecosystem as it first appears. It means getting used to the natural variability of the system over time. The importance of this long-term learning is in many ways harder to glean from industrial societies. Because the industrial process is fuelled by non-renewable energy sources and raw materials that are usually sourced from far afield, it is much more difficult to gauge when the systems that are relied on are being pressurised and made vulnerable.

What we now have to consider is whether the loss of resilience in ecosystems – which you have seen in 'peripheral' cases such as small islands and the Southern Ocean ecosystem – might now apply on a much larger scale. As industrial production, including industrialised agriculture, makes ever greater inroads into ecosystems around the planet, the issue of decreased resilience may now be at a global level. Our understanding of the ENSO and other major climatic oscillations, together with our growing knowledge of major catastrophic shifts such as the periodic break-up of the West Antarctic Ice Sheet, suggests that disruptions on a major scale are part of the normal workings of the planet – if it is viewed in the long term. This is the case, even without the human contribution to major geoclimatic change.

What we need to recognise is that intensifying human activity is increasing the likelihood of major disturbances at the same time that it is undermining the resilience of ecosystems around the planet. In this sense, it is not just the disasters of small islands or the Southern Ocean ecosystem that we have to keep in mind. It is also the responses to these events, and what we might learn from them. In particular, the way in which Antarctica and the ocean around it is being viewed as a kind of shared space – or 'commons' – for the globe might have implications on a far larger scale. Although the outcomes are far from perfect or complete, the processes of governance that have emerged from disputes over the southern polar regions and others may turn out to have had much broader implications for governing the planet as a whole.

While conflicts and negotiations over Antarctica and its seas began as a contest between colonial powers, you have seen that non-governmental organisations such as Greenpeace – which combine expert knowledge with broad-based popular support – have been able to exert an important influence. You have also seen that islands such as the Maldives have taken a stand on the global stage over global environmental changes that affect them. In Chapters 4 to 6 you gained further insights on the ways in which new electronic media allow you to gain direct access to data that you can use and manipulate to reach your own conclusions and develop your own arguments. These are all vital steps on the way to a broadened participation in governance – not only at a local level but also reaching out to encompass events of global significance.

Answers to Questions

Chapter 1

Question 1.1

Statements (b), (c) and (e) are misleadingly one-sided in their reading of globalisation; (a) and (d) give a more useful impression of the 'ambivalence' of globalisation.

Question 1.2

Your answer should be along the following lines. Increasing numbers of tourists require more facilities and services, which runs the risk of undermining the very scenic and environmental attractions that draw tourists to small islands. Unrestrained tourist development also places increasing demands on the environmental resources of a small island, which are not likely to be sustainable. You might also have mentioned the cultural impacts of tourism.

Question 1.3

Statements (a) and (d): sustainable development is intended to bridge the gap between developed and less-developed countries, without long-term damage to the environment, and without curtailing the growth of the already developed societies.

Question 1.4

Someone living in the British Isles will probably be attracted to the idea of slightly warmer temperatures, and everything this implies for lifestyle. A person living in the Maldives who is aware of the link between warming and sea-level rise is more likely to take a dim view of even a slight change. However, you might also consider that the British islander may be aware of the threat that sea-level change holds to low-lying parts of the British Isles, and that both 'respondents' might have a 'global' awareness of the impact of warming on people elsewhere.

Question 1.5

The obvious examples are coastal erosion and the saltwater contamination of freshwater aquifers. Another possible answer is that rising sea levels also worsen the effects of storms – especially when there are storm surges – and the effects of rare events such as tsunamis.

Question 1.6

Your answer should include the following points: 10 years is too short a time to capture long-term trends; one island is not a large enough sample to represent an entire region, and certainly cannot represent the whole planet; because climate varies naturally, the demonstration of a warming trend does not necessarily point to human impact.

Question 1.7

Of the seven points, (a)–(d) could account for an observed increase in relative or absolute sea level. More specifically, (e) is a correct statement but gives the impression of falling sea levels at localities affected by deglaciation; (f) is an incorrect statement since the removal of ice sheets would lead to isostatic uplift, not subsidence – see (e); (g) the generation of new land through tectonic activity (uplift of the sea floor) is likely to give the impression of falling sea levels at that locality.

Question 1.8

The three main factors are volcanic activity; the upheaval and deformation of rocks and sediments caused by continental plates colliding; and the accretion or build-up of coral reef colonies from the bodies of small marine organisms. You might also have mentioned that decreasing sea level can bring a previously submerged region of the sea floor into the sub-aerial environment. (You may also have heard of islands 'built up' from accumulated bird excrement or 'guano', such as those off the coast of Peru, or elsewhere as atolls in the South Pacific Ocean.)

Question 1.9

Statements (b), (c) and (e) each suggest a misunderstanding of uncertainty; (b) ignores the fact that some forms of uncertainty are an inevitable consequence of the way some systems work in the physical world; (c) overlooks the fact that the physical world can give rise to genuine novelty, which inevitably involves uncertainty; (e) fails to consider the potential for decision makers to account for uncertainty by building it into the decision-making process.

Question 1.10

Statements (a) and (e) are true; (b) takes the term 'catastrophe' too literally, and ignores the fact that catastrophic changes happen all around us on many scales – without necessarily having undesirable effects; (c) is incorrect because changes tend to be sudden, with few visible signs that they are imminent; (d) misses the point that systems of this kind tend to drive toward one state or another, the intermediate positions being highly unstable and transient.

Chapter 2

Question 2.1

Statements (a) and (c) are correct; (b) is incorrect because smaller ecosystems, such as ponds or creeks, are part of larger ecosystems, such as wetlands or river systems, which implies that an organism can be part of ecosystems on several different scales; (d) is incorrect because both organic and inorganic matter is exchanged with surrounding systems; (e) is incorrect because human beings are part of the ecosystems they live in, and because social systems interlink with ecosystems in many ways.

Question 2.2

(a) Fresh food; (b) fresh water; (c) timber, for ship repairs, etc.; (d) a place for rest and recuperation; (e) an island was also a meeting place where different crews could exchange information and commodities.

Question 2.3

Deforestation left soil exposed, resulting in erosion. Eroded soil silted up rivers and harbours and contaminated freshwater supplies. It was widely conjectured (correctly) that deforestation could alter local climates ('microclimates'). There was some understanding of the role of forests in forming mist and precipitating rain, so deforestation was linked to declining rainfall.

Question 2.4

(a) Its behaviour was 'naive' (that is, it lacked the experience of predators that would have made it more cautious and defensive).

(b) It was flightless.

(c) It was ground-nesting.

(d) Its reproduction rate was relatively slow (only one egg per clutch).

Question 2.5

Governance encompasses all the many ways in which people influence the steering and management of their societies. It includes the processes by which ordinary people at the 'bottom' or 'grassroots' level of their societies make contributions, as well as the procedures undertaken by people in positions of greater power. Government implies the directing and managing of society from 'above', usually by small groups who specialise in decision making and power wielding.

Question 2.6

The correct historical sequence is: (c), (b), (f), (e), (d), (a).

Question 2.7

Statements (a), (c) and (d) are correct; (b) is incorrect, because the particular cluster of genes which a founder population brings with it to an island does not necessarily prepare it for the new environment; (e) is incorrect because the genetic range of the founder population is only the starting point for the new phase of evolutionary development. Subsequently, selection pressures play a major role.

Question 2.8

Human factors such as the overexploitation of species, habitat destruction and bioinvasion all weaken the resilience of a species, although it may survive immediate human impact. At some later stage, perhaps through several episodes, natural extremes or variability (such as drought or cyclone) may provide the stress that the species population cannot survive, resulting in extinction.

Question 2.9

While species introduced by Polynesian explorers may have come from other islands, some of these species were originally from the mainland (e.g. rats, pigs, dogs) and were, therefore, alien to oceanic islands. Their introduction probably led to severe degradation of ecosystems in many cases. Some species brought in from neighbouring islands may well have fitted into island ecosystems without major stress. However, keep in mind that island species have often diverged markedly, even from their relatives on neighbouring islands, so the risks of relocation may also be high. In general, though, organisms transplanted from within the vicinity of the new island probably have coevolved more easily with island ecosystems than organisms from further away.

Question 2.10

Statements (c) and (d) are correct; (a) is incorrect because it does not allow for coevolution between humans and other components of ecosystems over time; (b) is incorrect because it overrates the potential of culture and social organisation, ignoring the fact that social and cultural factors can inhibit as well as assist coevolution.

Chapter 3

Question 3.1

Statements (a), (b) and (e) are correct; (c) is incorrect because of the claim that complex systems have no external connections; (d) is incorrect because not all feedback loops stabilise the system. Moreover, many simple systems are very stable.

Question 3.2

This is an unwise strategy because the change from a reef dominated by coral to one dominated by macro-algae tends to be catastrophic rather than gradual. It means that there are likely to be few visible signs that conditions are building up to shift. By the time there is clear visible evidence of a takeover by macro-algae, it would probably be too late to reverse tourist development trends and prevent the shift happening.

Question 3.3

Reasons (c) and (d) are valid; (a) and (b) are incorrect because computer modelling can give very useful information about the real world, including the modelling of feedbacks, if its limitations are taken into account; (e) is incorrect because catastrophic shifts are not random and it is possible, at least hypothetically, to predict them.

Question 3.4

Statements (a) and (d) are correct; (b) is incorrect because it is impossible to prevent all disturbance and because all ecosystems have evolved to cope with certain levels of disturbance; (c) is incorrect because loss of redundancy increases the vulnerability to present and future disturbances.

Question 3.5

Statements (a), (c) and (d) are correct; (b) is incorrect because agricultural production involves many more reductions or simplifications of the ecosystem than it does additions.

Question 3.6

Statements (a) and (d) are correct; (b) is incorrect because the factors causing or 'forcing' the ENSO are distinct from those influencing the monsoon; (c) is misleading because it now seems that the ENSO only has a major influence on the monsoon during phase-locking; (e) is incorrect because phase-locking exacerbates the effects of the two systems, rather than cancelling them out.

Question 3.7

Actions (b), (d) and (f) are correct; (a) is incorrect as market forces are most likely to make food available to those who can pay for it, i.e. the least needy people; (c) is incorrect as maximising land use reduces redundancy in the system; (e) is incorrect as the most needy people are unlikely to have the economic resources to meet tax increases.

Question 3.8

An extreme rain deficit is likely to cause serious crop failure or reduction. An economic downturn will reduce the revenue earned from those crops that do make it on to the global market. These effects are likely to reinforce each other, making it extremely difficult for the farmer to recover from adversity.

Question 3.9

Examples (b), (c) and (d) are all top-down; it is important to recognise that top-down governance is not necessarily harmful. In (c) – redistribution of food between regions – it may only be state or provincial governors who have the capacity for this kind of response to adverse conditions. Example (a) is not top-down governance because it suggests a much more local, bottom-up form of decision making, although village-level decision making is not necessarily democratic or all-inclusive. Examples (e) and (f) are not top-down governance as they involve decisions at the local or individual level, including the decision to participate in a global market where it is freely taken and not enforced from above.

Question 3.10

The great differences in power and wealth between people who are drawn into global markets suggest an uneven 'playing field'. Climatic differences and other forms of environmental variability can also be viewed as a kind of unevenness.

Chapter 4

Question 4.1

The main feature of a coreless winter is that there is no definable minimum winter temperature. From summer to autumn, temperature falls rapidly, and then stays within a narrow range until spring. You do not see a coreless winter on the coast of Antarctica because of the close proximity of the ocean.

Question 4.2

An ice shelf is glacial ice that remains attached to the land but is floating on the ocean. This means that the ice displaces the same weight of water as it contains. As it melts, water is not added to the ocean and so sea level remains constant. (You can do this experiment yourself with a glass of water and some ice.)

Question 4.3

We cannot be sure. There are several competing claims, for example William Smith landed on King George Island in 1819, a British ship sighted and charted the Trinity Peninsula in 1820, and American and Russian ships also sighted the mainland at about the same time. In reality, Antarctica was almost certainly discovered by an unnamed sealing ship.

Question 4.4

In a Mercator projection lines of latitude are horizontal, and lines of longitude are vertical. If you draw the whole of Antarctica using this system, the region is very distorted and it is very hard to see the shape of the land. The South Pole cannot be represented as a point but only as the whole of the 180° S line of latitude. A polar projection is much more useful.

Question 4.5

(d) The USA has not made a territorial claim in Antarctica.

Question 4.6

Antarctica is fringed by ice shelves which continually calve icebergs. This means that, as each iceberg drifts away from Antarctica, it reduces the area of the continent slightly. This change can be more drastic when an entire ice shelf collapses.

Question 4.7

Antarctica was located at a southern latitude similar to that of Australia today. This means that it would have had a similar climate and be mostly ice-free.

Question 4.8

No: Britain is in the Northern Hemisphere and Antarctica is in the Southern, which means that the warmest temperatures are during the British winter.

Question 4.9

Glacial ice is formed from snow and so is made of freshwater.

Question 4.10

The ease of finding information on the internet makes it very tempting to use the first information that you find. It is important to try to get an idea of how 'good' and how 'current' your first source is.

Question 4.11

By carefully specifying your requirements for information you can be more specific about the information you require and thus not waste time on irrelevant or poor quality information.

Chapter 5

Question 5.1

The polar front acts as a barrier in the Southern Ocean with warmer water to the north. The island to the south will be surrounded by this cold water and its temperature will be reduced. The cold temperatures mean that precipitation can fall as snow and glaciers could grow. The island to the north of the polar front will be much warmer and any precipitation will fall as rain.

Question 5.2

The levels are: (a) killer whale – top carnivore; (b) penguin, (f) crabeater seal and (d) baleen whale – carnivores; (c) krill – mainly herbivores; (e) phytoplankton – primary producer (Figure A1). Humans would appear towards the top of the food web in a carnivore trophic level.

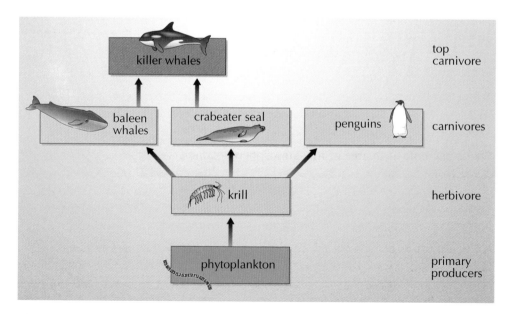

Figure A1   A simplified food web.

Question 5.3

Primary producers become entrained in the ice when the frazil ice develops into pancake ice and traps seawater in the ice matrix. This would happen when the ice is advancing, i.e. in the southern autumn and winter. From Figure 5.3, this would be generally from March to June.

Question 5.4

The raw materials for phytoplankton growth are not uniformly distributed around Antarctica, so phytoplankton growth is patchy. This means that as the frazil ice forms pancake ice, only those regions rich in phytoplankton will entrain a layer of chlorophyll.

Question 5.5

As sea ice is made of frozen seawater, when it retreats it will not affect sea level. The snow that is on top of the sea ice will contribute to a higher sea level but this is not significant.

Question 5.6

The blue whale can survive on krill for two reasons. First, there is a short food chain from primary producer to predator and so a significant amount of energy is transferred. Second, the krill exhibit swarming behaviour which concentrates many individuals in a small area. As a result, the whale can ingest huge numbers at once.

Question 5.7

Iron is thought to be the missing raw material that holds back biological production in large parts of the Southern Ocean. If iron could be added to the waters here, the theory is that primary producers could be stimulated into growth. As they grow, carbon dioxide would be used and possibly sucked from the atmosphere into the ocean. This could reduce or even stop the increase of atmospheric carbon dioxide, thus mitigating climate change.

Chapter 6

Question 6.1

The ozone hole is an area of low atmospheric ozone concentration in the stratosphere, centred over Antarctica. It is a problem because ozone absorbs ultraviolet light, which, if it reaches the Earth's surface, can damage living cells.

Question 6.2

An EIA must be carried out for any planned activity in Antarctica to assess the effects on the environment of that activity. A CEE is also carried out to assess the effects of an activity on the environment but only if those effects are considered to be anything more than minor.

Question 6.3

The Antarctic Treaty is an international agreement, signed in 1958, which came into effect in 1961. Under the Treaty, all new decisions about global policy south of 60° S must be made by unanimous agreement. The Antarctic Treaty System includes not only the Antarctic Treaty but also four further international agreements: Agreed Measures for the Conservation of Antarctic Fauna and Flora (1964); Convention for the Conservation of Antarctic Seals (1972); Convention for the Conservation of Antarctic Marine Living Resources (1982); and Protocol of Environmental Protection to the Antarctic Treaty (1998). CCAMLR controls the exploitation of the Antarctic marine environment south of the Antarctic Convergence – i.e. a much larger area than the original Antarctic Treaty, which only covers the area south of 60° S.

Question 6.4

Statement (d) is false because the British government controlled most of the whaling in the Southern Ocean and collected revenues from the whalers, although most of the whalers were Norwegian.

Question 6.5

(a) Whaling would tend to decrease population numbers, by increasing the predation rate on whales.

(b) The setting up of the International Whaling Commission in 1946, in itself, would have had no effect on whale numbers.

(c) The moratorium on whaling declared by the IWC in 1982 would have helped to increase whale numbers by reducing the predation rate.

(d) The decline of seal populations could have helped to increase whale numbers because the competition between whales and seals for food would be decreased.

(e) The lack of profit available from hunting when whale populations are very small would have helped to increase whale numbers because whaling stopped as a result of the low profits, thereby reducing the predation rate on whales.

(f) The readmission of Iceland to the IWC might be enough to swing the vote in favour of a resumption of whaling and, if this happens, whale numbers are likely to decrease.

Question 6.6

Statements (f) and (k) are false. No territorial claims in Antarctica are recognised under international law and the first long-term research programme in Antarctica was set up by Britain (the Discovery Investigations).

Question 6.7

(a) The Discovery Investigations took place in the 1920s. It was the first major research initiative in Antarctica and was very ambitious in its aims.

(b) The International Geophysical Year took place in 1957–8. It was an international collaboration, involving 67 countries, which resulted in a massive increase in scientific effort in the region and left a legacy in the form of a proliferation of Antarctic bases.

Question 6.8

The limitations are that imprecise articles create problems with interpretation, reaching consensus can take a long time, and the area south of 60° S does not include the whole Antarctic ecosystem (which includes all the area as far north as the polar front). It could be argued that (a) and (b) are strengths because the imprecise wording of Article IV puts all territorial disputes into abeyance for an indefinite time, and because every member of the ATS has equal voting rights regardless of how much money they put into Antarctic research.

Question 6.9

Statement (f) is false. The Protocol on Environmental Protection to the Antarctic Treaty did resolve the debate on whether to allow mining for mineral resources in Antarctica but only temporarily, by banning it for 50 years.

Question 6.10

(1) The discovery in 1985 by the British Antarctic Survey of the ozone hole, caused by the release to the atmosphere of synthetic chemicals such as CFCs, now controlled through the introduction of global legislation.

(2) The discovery in the 1970s of Lake Vostok and other freshwater lakes below the Antarctic ice cap. The water in Lake Vostok has been out of contact with the atmosphere for over 500 000 years and it could contain unique life forms. It could also present similar conditions to those found on Europa, the moon of Jupiter, which would make it a useful model for NASA, or any other agency planning to journey to Europa.

Question 6.11

Statement (a) is false. A scientific study of a penguin colony at Port Lockroy, which is visited very frequently by tourists, revealed no effects on the penguins compared with an undisturbed colony.

Acknowledgements

Grateful acknowledgement is made to the following sources:

Figures

Figure 1.1a: Getmapping; Figures 1.1b and 1.5: Bob Spicer; Figure 1.2: Bantam Press, a division of Transworld Publishers Ltd, 1990/Bantam Books, a division of Bantam Doubleday Dell Publishing Group, Inc., 1990, © John and Mary Gribbin, 1990; Figures 1.3, 1.6, 1.10, 2.1, 3.2, 3.7, 3.8, 3.10b and 3.15: Marion Hall; Figures 1.4, 1.9, 1.11, 2.7, 4.1, 4.158, 4.16, 4.17, 5.4, 5.11, 5.14, 5.15, 6.2, 6.5, 6.7b, 6.15, 6.16 and 6.17: Mark Brandon; Figure 1.7: Andy Crump/Still Pictures; Figure 1.8: Imagestate/Pictor; Figure 1.14: Lloyd Homer, copyright Institute of Geological and Nuclear Sciences Ltd; Figure 2.2: Kim Crosbie; Figure 2.4: Copyright The Natural History Museum, London; Figure 2.5: Shelburne Museum, Shelburne, Vermont; Figure 2.8: Pyne, S. J. (1997) *Vestal Fire: An Environmental History, told through fire of Europe and Europe's encounter with the world.* University of Washington Press; Figure 2.9: Herb Kawainui Kane; Figure 2.10: Courtesy of Pro Chile; Figure 3.1: Florida Keys National Marine Sanctuary Staff; Figure 3.3: International Stock/Robert Harding; Figure 3.4: Ursula Keuper-Bennett/Peter Bennett TURTLE TRAX; Figure 3.6: National Oceanic and Atmospheric Administration/Department of Commerce; Figures 3.9 and 3.11: Davis, M. (2001) *Late Victorian Holocausts*, Verso; Figure 3.10a: Darius Klemens/Link; Figure 3.13: Ilay Cooper/Images of India/Link; Figure 3.14: www.lacma.org/Uttar Pradesh; Figure 4.3: Royal Geographical Society; Figure 4.4: Center for Astrophysical Research in Antarctica, University of Chicago Department of Astronomy and Astrophysics; Figure 4.6: MODIS images courtesy of NASA's Terra satellite, supplied by Ted Scambos, National Snow and Ice Data Center, University of Colorado, Boulder; Figure 4.8: By permission of The British Library; Figure 4.9: Bryan and Cherry Alexander Photography; Figure 4.10: Adapted from Walton, D. W. H. (ed.) (1987), *Antarctic Science.* Cambridge University Press; Figure 4.13: Science Museum/Science and Society Picture Library; Figure 4.14: Golonka, J. and Ford, D. (2000) 'Pangean (Late Carboniferous-Middle Jurassic) palaeonvironment and lithofacies', *Palaeogeography, Palaeoclimatology, Palaeoecology.* Elsevier Science; Figure 5.1: National Oceanic and Atmospheric Administration; Figure 5.2: Courtesy of Pablo Clemente-Colon, U.S. National Ice Center; Figure 5.3: Zwally, H. Jay et al. (2002), 'Variability of Antarctic sea ice 1979–1998', *Journal of Geophysical Research*, Vol. 107, C5. Copyright © American Geophysical Union; Figure 5.5: © Kevin Hughes; Figure 5.6a: Steve Turner/OSF; Figure 5.6b: Kim Crosbie; Figure 5.7a: © Julian Priddle/Science Training and Education Partnership; Figure 5.7b: NASA; Figure 5.9: The British Antarctic Survey; Figure 5.10: Tynan, C. T. (1998) 'Ecological importance of the Southern Boundary of the Antarctic Circumpolar Current', *Nature*, Vol. 392, 16 April 1998. © Macmillan Magazines Ltd; Figure 5.12: Aflo Foto Agency/Photolibrary;

Figure 6.1: Scott Polar Research Institute; Figures 6.3 and 6.4: Hardy, A. Sir (1967) *Great Waters*. HarperCollins Publishers. Copyright © Sir Alister Hardy.; Figures 6.6 and 6.9: Sullivan, W. (1957) *Quest for a Continent*. Secker & Warburg; Figure 6.7a: ADAGP, Paris and DACS, London; Figure 6.13: © 1998 Greenpeace Communications Ltd; Figure 6.14: NASA.

Index

Entries and page numbers in **bold** are glossary terms. Page numbers in *italics* refer to information in Figures and Tables.